'Bravest Cat in the World' Has Died in the City

"Evening News" Reporter

FAITH, the "bravest cat in the world," has died. This announcement was posted to-day in the tower of the church of St. Augustine and St. Faith under St. Paul's in Watling - street, City.

It was in September, 1940. Bombs falling on the City shattered the rectory where Faith, a stray cat, was nursing her kitten. Fire and water and ruin were all round her but she remained calm and waited for help.

The Rev. R. Ross, the vicar, went into the ruined church and rescued her and her kitten. He was with her too, when, after becoming unconscious, she died, aged 14.

The People's Dispensary for Sick Animals of the Poor awarded a certificate recording her bravery and struck a special medal for her. Through the Humane Society of New York she was awarded the Paddy Reilly Medal of Honour.

Faith's kitten is now a big Tom named Panda and living in a nursing home in Herne Hill.

Rosamond M. Young

Two Perfectly Marvellous Cats

A True Story

✦

Rosamond M. Young

J. N. Townsend Publishing
Exeter, New Hampshire
1996

Printed in the United States by BookCrafters.

Jacket illustrations by Judith Roberts-Rondeau.
Jacket and text design by Martha E. Raines.

Published by: J. N. Townsend Publishing
                 12 Greenleaf Drive
                 Exeter, NH 03833
                 603-778-9883
                 800-333-9883

Library of Congress Cataloging-in-Publication Data
Young, Rosamond McPherson.
        Two perfectly marvellous cats : a true story /
Rosamond M. Young.
            p. cm.
        Includes bibliographical references.
        ISBN 1-880158-12-4
        1. World War, 1939-1945—Great Britain. 2. Cats--
Great Britain—Biography. 3. World War, 1939-194—
Medals—Great Britain. I. Title.
D810.A65Y68   1996   96-8039
940.53'41—dc20   CIP

Contents

Foreword

One day in 1993 Joyce McLennan, a friend who lives in London, saw an announcement in a London newspaper about an auction at Christie's. Among the items to be auctioned was a medal that had been awarded to a cat. The Dickin Medal was expected to bring 3,000 pounds. Joyce, who is a cat person, clipped the article and sent it to me, another cat person.

I was intrigued. How did a cat happen to receive a medal? The newspaper clipping said that the medal had been given in 1949 by the People's Dispensary for Sick Animals, to Simon, the ship's cat on the *Amethyst*, an English frigate.

Off I went to the public library. I found the story about the *Amethyst* but nothing about Simon.

My granddaughter, Rosemary O'Toole, lives in London. I asked her to see what she could find out about the medal from the PDSA, as it is commonly called. She rang the London office and was referred to the national headquarters in Telford, Shropshire. From there Isabel George sent her a packet of information.

The Dickin Medal, named for the founder of the PDSA Maria Dickin, was presented to animals displaying conspicuous gallantry or devotion to duty associated with the armed forces or civil defense during World War II and its aftermath. Dickin Medals were given to 53 animals—18 dogs, 3 horses, 31 pigeons and 1 cat.

One cat? *One* cat?

That sounded like a good story.

I packed my bag and flew to London and took a train to Shrewsbury, the nearest town to Telford in Shropshire with a good hotel.

While I was conferring with Gill Hubbard there, she said, "Simon is the only cat who received the Dickin, but there was another cat you ought to know about."

"Who was that?"

Gill produced a photograph and some leaflets. "Her name was Faith. She was a church cat in London, and during the Blitz she did a very brave deed. She was not eligible for the Dickin, because she was a civilian cat, but Mrs. Dickin was so impressed with what she did that she had a special silver medal struck for her."

That sounded like another good story.

Following a suggestion from Isabel George, I visited Lieutenant Commander Stewart Hett, president of the *Amethyst* Association, at his home in Middlesex and saw his scrapbooks and a movie shot he had made on board ship of Simon drinking milk out of a bowl.

Staff members of The Imperial War Museum in London were exceedingly helpful also, producing the scrapbooks of Captain John S. Kerans, of the *Amethyst,* which include many clippings about Simon. The museum made photographs of Faith and Simon available.

Three friends, Millie Bingham, Catharine Booker, and Freda Stohrer read the manuscript and made so many suggestions I had to write the book over ten times, I hope to its improvement.

The Reverend Gordon S. Price was the advisor on subjects ecclesiastical. George and Cynthia Gibbs made a trip to the PDSA cemetery at Ilford and made photographs of Simon's grave.

All these people made possible this story of two absolutely marvellous cats, and I thank them.

Rosamond M. Young

Part One

✦

Faith:
Dear Little Church Cat

The Parting

September 1936

*H*er foot itched. She bent over and licked the top of it, splaying out her toes like a fan.

"Move over." The woman nudged her with her shoe, a flat-heeled brown health oxford with black laces. The gray tabby moved from the center of the top step to the edge.

With green-eyed curiosity she had been watching the man and woman carry boxes out of the house.

Now the man staggered out with a cardboard box almost too big for him, tied with a piece of rope. The woman followed him down the weedy path with a market basket over one arm piled with odds and ends of plates, cups, and bowls. In the other hand she grasped two frying pans.

They stowed the box, the dishes and the pans into the pickup truck in the street. On the side of the truck in faded letters a sign read:

Light Hauling

Joe Burns

Removals

They walked back up the graveled path to the house.

It was a gray day in London in September, 1936. Signs of the Depression were everywhere: unpainted houses, weeds in the gardens, empty cottages with broken windows.

Joe Burns had made a fair living with his truck for many years, but the Depression had put an end to it. Now he came out of the house and stood looking for the last time at what had been their home. He wore a blue pullover with raveled elbows, a pair of brown tweed trousers that had taken on his shape, bowed legs and all, and dull, brown brogans. He reached down and stroked the cat's back, letting her black-ringed tail flow through his fingers. "It's too bad, Puss. I wish we could take you with us." He and his wife would live with their son in an East End tenement apartment until times got better. No pets were permitted there.

The cat had lived with Joe and his wife since a year before when she wandered to their door, a hungry, white-chested gray kitten, born in a warehouse on a dock along the Thames. They took her in, and she had been happy with them. They fed her little bits of fish and once in a while a piece of chicken. She caught mice and spiders and grasshoppers in the garden. She also caught pointy-nosed shrews and voles, but she didn't eat them.

The woman came out with a chipped plate and a tin cup in her hands. She set them down on the step. "Here, Puss, a nice piece of fish and a cup of water. It's the best we can do for you."

The cat walked to the plate and daintily smelled the fish. Then she settled down and began to eat. The woman bent over and stroked the cat's back. "I hate to do this to her," she said to her husband. She straightened up. "Leave the key in the door for whoever moves in. Maybe they'll keep her."

They walked down the path, shut the sagging gate behind them and climbed into the old truck. The engine coughed into life, and they drove away, one wheel on the truck wobbling.

The cat looked up from her food and watched the car disappear down the narrow street. Then she finished the fish and sat looking at the street while she licked her lips to get every crumb. She began to wash herself, behind her ears, her chest, the insides of her back legs, her four white feet, and finally her tail. She crouched down on the step, curled her tail around her and closed her eyes.

No Cats Here!

*H*ours later cold drops of rain splatting on her back woke her. She stood up, stretched, and meowed at the door, but it remained closed. The rain flattened her thick fur and chilled her skin. She trotted on a walk made of old boards around the side of the house out to the coal shed. The door to the shed had long ago rotted away, but inside she would at least be out of the rain. She shook herself as she stepped out of the weather and looked around. Nothing was left in the shed except a few lumps of coal and some old kindling sticks the woman had picked up along the railroad tracks.

Sometimes the cat caught a mouse here. She walked hopefully around the walls, sniffing and listening, but all she could hear was the rain beating on the tin roof. She squatted down on the wooden floor and tucked her paws under her. She would wait for them to come home. A great many hours of her life had been spent in waiting.

When she woke the next morning, she hurried around to the front window of the house and standing on her hind legs, peered inside and meowed. She saw no light and no shadows of the man or woman moving inside the house. The empty dish still sat on the doorstep, and rain had filled the tin cup.

The truck was not parked at the curb.

She waited all day for them to come back. She caught a spider and a grasshopper in the weeds, but she was still hungry.

She stayed another night in the coal shed.

When morning came and still the door remained shut, she set out along the street. She was hungrier than ever, and she longed for a warm place by a fire. She stopped and meowed at doors along the street, but no knob turned, no door opened. At one place a woman with a broom in her hand was standing in her open door, and when the cat turned in at the gate, she hurled the broom like a javelin and shouted "Scat!" The cat bounded off, her tail drooping and ears flat against her head.

She arrived at Watling Street where automobiles and buses whisked by, stirring up air that smelled of gasoline and smoke. Tires screeched. Horns blared. Brakes squealed. These offended her ears, and the rushing cars frightened her. She sat watching the street for a long time, but it never seemed safe to try to cross.

She turned to her left and keeping close to the buildings that stood along the pavement, she plodded along, shrinking away from the heavy shoes and high heels of people passing by. In front of one building lay drifts of papers in untidy heaps, smelling of grease and fish. She stopped to nose at the papers. Fish! The smell made her stomach churn. She pawed through the papers and found three bites of fish and a sliver of potato. She ate them rapidly and sniffed in vain for more.

When she was sure there was no more food, she continued along the store fronts until she came to a small park with thick, springy grass that felt good to her paws. She caught two grasshoppers and crawled under a bush to take a nap.

Another cold rain dripping through the leaves woke her, soaking her gray back and striking through to her skin. Oh, to find an open door and a warm room!

She left the park and continued down the busy street.

A tall building stood a short way off the street. Up three steps she saw an open door. Men and women, walking up the steps, disappeared through the doorway.

The cat bounded up the steps and hid behind one of the doors, which opened out onto the porch. Pleasant fragrances drifted out from the open doorway. Finally when no more people came up the steps, she stepped out from behind the door and slipped into the building.

Warmth caressed her damp fur. She crept along the wall. A sound she had never heard before filled the great room, and the people stood up and began singing. She had heard singing before. The woman used to sing around the house.

The little cat sank down on the stone floor, and as the warmth of the great room penetrated into her muscles and bones, all the tenseness went out of her body, and she closed her eyes and slept, her chin on one paw.

"A cat!" exclaimed a deep voice. "Who invited you to come in here?"

She lifted her head with a startled cry. Strong hands closed around her body before she could move and hoisted her into the air. Holding her prisoner in his hands, the man strode to the doorway and tossed her outside. "Off with you! Scat! We don't allow cats in here."

He closed the door.

Cats Don't Give Up

The cat walked to the top step of the porch and sat down. It had been warm inside and dry. Out here it was cold, and the rain had begun once more. Perhaps the door would open again.

Hunger clawed at her. She set out again into the street where the cars screeched by, and the boots with thick soles tramped along the pavement. She came to the place she had passed before where people dropped papers that still had bits of fish in them.

As she approached the fish and chips shop, her tail dragging almost to the pavement, a pair of boots came out of the shop. The cat looked up at the owner of the boots and meowed. He glanced down and saw her.

"Hungry, are you, Pussy?" She rolled over on her back and looked up at him with pleading eyes. He broke off a piece of fish and put it down on the pavement.

It was as big as a mouse. The man stood eating his fish and chips out of a paper, and the cat ate her fish at his feet. When he set off down the street, she followed him, but he disappeared among the forest of legs at the corner, where their owners waited for the traffic light to change.

She plodded back to the church porch and waited by the door.

She waited and waited and waited. At last the door opened, and a few people came out. She whipped around the edge of the door and hurried inside, creeping along the wall. Oh, the wonderful heat!

A pair of shiny boots came down the aisle. "I thought I put you out once!" exclaimed the voice she had heard before. The man picked her up and carried her to the door. "Now out with you! We don't want cats here." He put her down on the slate floor of the porch. "And don't come back here again."

She dodged between his legs and ran back inside, her ears flat against her head. He chased her. She was not quick enough to escape his grabbing hands. He picked her up roughly and carried her to the edge of the porch. He aimed his toe at her, but she dodged away.

When the door closed, she crept into a corner behind the door out of the rain and settled down to wait.

A long time passed before the doors opened again. This time she scurried into the warmth along with the people coming in from the street. She hid in a dark corner and grew drowsy as the heat from the room once more wrapped around her. After a time the people left, and only two pairs of boots remained standing by the doorway, boots almost hidden by long robes with trimming like the window curtains at the house where she had lived. The doors closed and the two men walked between the rows of benches, and soon the lights began to go out.

She waited until she could hear no more footsteps. Then she crept away from the wall and sprang onto a long bench. The bench was cushioned, and she began kneading the soft fabric, which made her think of her mother's body, long, long ago. She turned around on the cushion and sank down into it.

Faith

In the morning when daylight came through the stained glass windows, making colored patches on the floor, she stepped off the cushion to the floor and stretched her forelegs in front of her as far as they would reach, spreading her paws like little white fans. Then she stood and stretched her back legs, one at a time, reaching as far back as she could.

She sat down and washed herself, face, ears, chest, paws and inside her back legs. All the stiffness from the cold rains had gone. She was hungry.

She tested the air with her nose.

Food!

Someone was cooking something. She followed the scent.

Up a stairway she came to an open door.

Two men stood in front of a fireplace where a wood fire snapped and hissed. They both were drinking something from cups they held in their hands. She recognized their voices. They were the men she had seen last night; one was the man who had tossed her out into the street.

She walked up to them and spoke.

"Well, look who's here," exclaimed the other man, looking down at her. "Where did you come from, Puss?"

The man who had thrown her out set down his cup and reached to pick her up. She backed away. "It's a stray that has been hanging around here. I put her out three times yesterday. Here she is, back again. I don't know how she got in this morning."

"Maybe she came when you did."

"I would have seen her. She probably slipped in last night at Evening Prayer."

"Maybe she's a parishioner. I think she looks like an Anglican cat."

"Father Ross! Cats don't belong to churches. What do they know about religion?" He reached for her, but she eluded him. "Help me catch her. I'll put her out."

"Cats don't have religion? Oh, my dear Thomas, do you know the poem by Christopher Smart about his cat Jeffrey? 'For I will consider my cat Jeffrey, For he is the servant of the living God, duly and daily serving him, For at the first glance of the glory of God in the East, he worships in his way.' That's the way it begins. Have you read it?"

"No."

"Have you ever heard of Christopher Smart?"

"No."

"He was an eighteenth century poet, born in Kent. Educated at Cambridge. I studied him in a lit course. He translated Horace, and wrote 'The Song of David.' Nobody remembers him now, except for the poem about his cat. I'll look it up and leave it on your desk."

"Thank you."

Henry Ross, a slim, neat man with straight brown hair combed over the dome of his forehead, blue eyes, and a deep, warm voice, reached out a hand the proper way, with fingers curled, inviting the cat to smell them. She stepped close to his hand, and he stroked her on the back. She let him pick her up. "She's very thin," he said. "She hasn't been eating well. Have we anything to give her?"

"No, we don't. If you feed her, she'll keep hanging around. You'll never get rid of her."

"There's that little pitcher of cream for our coffee," said Henry. "Cats like cream. Pour some out in my saucer."

"Father Ross, if you feed her, she won't want to leave."

"Don't you like cats?"

Thomas Evans, the verger, looked troubled. He was gray-haired with an enormous gray mustache that swept out over his cheeks and joined his sideburns so that he always seemed to be smiling even when he was not. He shrugged. "But my wife Rosalind loves them." He always spoke of her as "my wife Rosalind," as if he had several others he did not mention. "I was just trying to save trouble. St. Augustine's has never had a cat."

"Pour her some cream."

He poured a little bit of cream into his saucer and set it down on the stone floor in front of the hearth. When Henry put the cat down, she sniffed at the saucer and settled down in front of it, bending over, her tongue flicking in and out, lapping up the cream.

Soon the saucer was empty. The cat looked up hopefully at the rector, who added a little more cream from the pitcher. After she emptied the saucer again, he picked her up and cradling her in his arms, looked into her light green eyes. She gazed steadily back at him.

"She must belong to somebody because she is so trusting," Henry said. "I'll put a lost notice in the church bulletin. She can stay with me upstairs in the rectory until her people come for her."

"But think of the trouble. She will need a bed and a litter box. And food and water."

"I'll ask the altar guild women to provide some things."

He carried the cat down to the next floor where the altar guild women had a meeting room.

Rosalind Evans, the verger's wife, a blonde, smiling woman with long, straight hair streaming out of a French twist, took the cat from Henry Ross and hugged it to her. "Look at her. Isn't she pretty? Where did she come from?"

"I don't know. Thomas thinks she walked in off the street at Evening Prayer. She doesn't have a collar. I don't even know if she's a girl, although I've been speaking of her as one."

Rosalind tipped up the cat's tail. "Yes, she's a girl. I hope she isn't a pregnant girl."

"Pregnant?" Henry's face turned pink. "I never gave that a thought."

"Of course you didn't, you poor, dear innocent man. But nine times out of ten, a female cat off the street is pregnant. What's to be done with her?"

"I'm going to put a notice in the bulletin. She must belong to somebody. She can stay here until her people come for her. I thought you might fix her a bed in a box or something and I'll look after her in the rectory upstairs until somebody claims her. We had a cat at home when I was a boy. "

"Where will she eat?"

"Would down here in the kitchen be all right with you?"

Rosalind nodded. "I know where there are some bowls for food and water. Cats should eat twice a day. They will eat more often if you let them, but we'd best start her in with good eating habits from the beginning."

Henry nodded and went off to write the notice.

The other two altar guild women, Ruth Taylor and Clara Brown, took turns holding the cat. Ruth did all the silver polishing at the church, and Clara ironed the vestments and altar cloths and kept them in repair. Rosalind supervised the others, since she was the verger's wife.

Next Sunday a notice appeared in the church bulletin:

Found

Gray and White Female Tabby Cat

Friendly, Talkative, Affectionate

Owner May Claim from

Henry Ross, Rector

St. Augustine and St. Faith Church near St. Paul's.

A month went by, but nobody claimed her or even asked about her.

"I have decided to keep the cat," Henry told Thomas at the end of the month. "Every church should have a cat," he explained. "I wouldn't be surprised if we have mice in the basement."

"I've never been down there."

"Paul Maguire stores the extra sheet music there." Paul was the organist and choir master.

"I didn't know that."

"I've been thinking about a name for our new cat."

"Have you decided what you are going to call her?"

"Yes. I think I'll name her Faith. In the first place this church is named St. Augustine and St. Faith, and she will be the church cat. Besides, even after you threw her out three times, she had the faith to come back here and try again."

The verger's face turned pink above the smile of his mustache.

The altar guild women rejoiced that Faith was going to stay. In addition to doing the silver and the linens and vestments, they also prepared lunch for the rector, the verger, and themselves, and they didn't mind a bit adding Faith to the guest list.

Rosalind brought a basket from home for Faith, and Ruth, who was short and fat with lively brown eyes, made a cushion to fit inside it. Clara, tall and lean, did ceramics and made a food bowl and a water bowl with a flower design and "Faith" inscribed under the glazing.

Faith settled in and explored every part of the church from the third floor rectory where she and Father Henry Ross lived to the basement. One day Paul Maguire accidentally left the basement door open when he took a load of music down, and Faith went right down behind him. She caught a mouse in the basement and brought it upstairs to Henry.

"You are a wonderful cat," Henry told her every day when he groomed her, and she grew sleek and a little bit fat from the wonderful food the women fixed for her.

Faith attended all services at which Henry was the preacher or the celebrant. She sat in the front pew except when Henry preached. Then she accompanied him to the pulpit and lay at his feet while he spoke. At the Eucharist she walked with the parishioners to the altar rail and when Henry came down the row with the host or the wine, he reached into the pocket of his robe and gave her a little tidbit that Clara baked for her.

The parishioners loved her, and sometimes she walked down the rows during the services, rubbing against the legs and sniffing the delicious smell of the shoes. She did not join in the hymns. Even Thomas took to patting her when he thought no one was looking. "By the way," he said to Henry one day. "I read the Christopher Smart poem you put on my desk. I liked the line that said `For he purrs when God tells him he is a good cat.'"

Henry smiled. "Faith is a good cat, and you're a good verger."

Four years passed by happily, and then came a change.

Panda

One day at lunch in August, 1940, Rosalind said to Clara and Ruth, "Do you notice anything unusual about Faith?"

Ruth looked down at Faith, who was having her lunch near the stove. Her gray back with the black stripes look soft and sleek. "Can't say that I do. Unusual in what way? She seems like always to me."

Clara reached down and picked her up. "She may have gained a little weight." She set her down again.

"I could be wrong," Rosalind remarked, "but I think our dear little Faith is about to become a mother."

"A mother!" exclaimed Clara. "How could that be? She never goes outside the church."

Rosalind tossed her head. "I had cats for years when I was a girl, and I think I know a pregnant cat when I see one. She may have got out one night at the wrong time. Or a wandering Tom may have got into the church."

"That's shocking to think of something like that going on right in the church," said Ruth. "Are you going to tell the rector?"

"One doesn't talk about such things with the rector. Besides, he has enough trouble just now with the war and shortages and rationing. No, I think we should just wait and let nature take its course. Besides, I could be wrong."

"We'll keep mum about it," said Ruth, and Clara nodded like a conspirator.

Faith finished her lunch and after washing herself, climbed the stairs to the rectory for her afternoon nap.

Everyone in England had things to worry about those days in 1940.

In January bacon, butter, and sugar were rationed. In April Germany invaded Holland, Luxembourg, and Belgium. Henry and Thomas joined the Home Guards in May. The Dutch army surrendered May

14, and two weeks later Belgian forces laid down their arms.

British forces evacuated at Dunkirk June 3, the Germans entered Paris on the fourteenth, and France fell to the invaders June 22. German tanks moved into the Netherlands and Denmark with little opposition.

On July 10 German bombers attacked British ships in the channel and in coastal harbors, damaging naval stations and factories. On the first day of fighting 100 aircraft engaged in dogfights over Dover, and German bombs fell on railways and ships and blew up munitions factories.

July dragged into August with nightly air raids over the coast. Next it would be London's turn to be bombed. Bomb shelters were ready and stocked; windows in houses and public buildings were covered with black blinds; the civil defense forces kept constant watch and patrolled the streets waiting, waiting, waiting.

When Henry woke one morning in the middle of August, Faith did not hop up on his bed and begin meowing for her breakfast as she usually did. Puzzled, he walked to her basket. She was still in it, and with her was one kitten, a wee little thing with its eyes closed. It was a white kitten with black ears and a black tail.

Henry went down on his knees beside the basket. "Why, Faith," he said, stroking her soft fur, "I didn't know you were going to become a mother." Faith looked up at him with pride in her green eyes.

Henry got to his feet and hurried to the rectory door. Over the stairway railing he called, "Thomas, are you here yet?"

The verger poked his head out of the study on the floor below. "I'm here. Coffee's ready."

"I want you to come up. Are the women here yet?"

"My wife Rosalind is here."

"Bring her and come. Something has happened."

Thomas and Rosalind came up the stairs, both puffing. "What is it?" asked Thomas. "Nothing bad, I hope?"

"Quite the contrary." Henry led them to the basket.

Rosalind dropped to her knees. "A kitten. Oh, look at it. Isn't it a dear little thing?" She checked through the basket. "But there seems to be only one. That's unusual, but I know it happens." She picked up the little bit of warm fur fluff, not even as long as her fingers. "Don't fret, Faith. I won't hurt your baby."

She put the kitten back in the basket, snug against Faith's body. "It's a boy," she told the two men.

"If only there wasn't a war on, I would ring the church bells," said Henry. They all knew no church bells in London could be rung except to announce an invasion.

While Henry shaved and dressed, Thomas and Rosalind went back downstairs.

Cora and Ruth had come in. When they heard the good news, Cora brought out some biscuits from the cupboard, and they were all on their second cup when Henry joined them.

He said, "I have been thinking about what to name the kitten. He is mostly white with a little bit of black like Chi Chi, the Giant Panda at the Zoo. What do you think of calling him Panda?"

"Splendid idea!" exclaimed Rosalind. "The perfect name."

Henry blushed, and Cora and Ruth nodded their agreement.

"Thomas, there's a bottle of hazelnut cordial in the cupboard. Bring it, and we'll celebrate Panda's arrival with a little in our coffee."

They sat around the table for half an hour, celebrating.

Henry drew a sign with colored pens announcing the birth of Panda and put it up on a pillar in the parish hall. At services the next Sunday the choir boys sang "All Things Bright and Beautiful" in Panda's honor.

Moving Day

On the morning of Friday, September 6, Henry sat at his desk working on the sermon for Sunday. The rectory was quiet although he could hear the sounds of ammunition trucks rolling past the church. Londoners had been warned to expect German bombers over the city at any time. They went about the work as always, but whenever they went outdoors, they kept watching the skies uneasily, and always they listened for the air raid sirens.

Henry felt a soft paw on his leg. He reached down and felt Faith's soft fur under his hand. "Meow."

He looked down at her and patted her head. She sat on her haunches, her head tipped up to him and her light green eyes staring unblinkingly into his.

He went back to his manuscript. Again he felt the paw on his trouser leg again, this time a little more insistent.

"What do you want, Faith?"

Faith walked to the door and looked back at him.

He put down his pen and walked to the door. Down the steps she went to the first floor and then to the ground floor, looking over her shoulder occasionally to be sure he was following. At the closed door to the steps that led to the basement, she stood on her hind paws and grasped at the doorknob with her front paws. She was not tall enough to reach the knob. She sat down and looked around at him. "You want the door open?"

"Meow."

Henry opened the door part way. She slipped through it and disappeared down the stairway.

"That's odd."

Henry went back to his study on the second floor.

Some time later he and Thomas were lunching in the dining room when Faith walked past the open doorway. Her head was high, and she had grabbed Panda by the scruff of his neck and was carrying him. His hind legs almost dragged on the floor, and his forepaws stuck out at odd angles, but he was not protesting.

"Now what is that cat up to?" Thomas asked, going to the doorway. He watched while Faith and Panda disappeared down the steps to the ground floor. "She is taking Panda downstairs," he said, shaking his head as he returned to the table.

"Maybe she is going to teach him to walk up the steps," Henry observed. "Or hunt for mice."

About three o'clock when he had finished his day's work on the sermon, Henry went upstairs to his living quarters to change his clothes before going out on his afternoon calls to visit sick parishioners. Faith's basket was empty.

It was still empty when he came back from his calls two hours later, and after changing his jacket for a pullover, he went down to the kitchen to heat water for tea. Everyone else had gone home.

When Faith heard him stirring in the kitchen, she came in for her dinner. Rosalind had left Faith's evening meal in the refrigerator, and Henry gave it to her. When she finished and had washed herself, Henry noticed her turn toward the stairway to the ground floor rather than go up to the living quarters on the top floor, and he decided to follow her.

Down the steps she went and to the still opened
door to the basement. Down the dark basement steps
she went with Henry after her. By the time he reached
the bottom of the steps, she had disappeared.

It was dark in the basement, but a weak light
came in through the window wells below the street
level. The civil defense officer had said it was not
necessary to put blackout curtains over the basement
windows since nobody ever went down there anyhow.

Everywhere he looked Henry could see stacks of
books, old prayer books the church no longer used, and
piles of music. The basement was large and dark and
cold. Henry shivered as he walked between the stacks of
music and books, calling Faith and listening for her
answer.

At last in the far corner he found her crouched
down in a gap between two stacks of music. And curled
up between her front legs sat Panda.

"I've heard cats moved their kittens around
sometimes," Henry said to her. "But why in the world
would you drag Panda down into this dark, old, dusty,
dirty cellar?"

He knelt down and picked up Panda. "Come on,
Faith, let's go back upstairs to your basket."

Carrying Panda, Henry climbed up the three flights of stairs, with Faith following and yowling all the way. "I'm not hurting your precious baby," said Henry. He put the kitten back into the basket and Faith climbed in beside him and licked him all over.

Henry conducted Evensong later that afternoon, and Faith did not go with him. She had been irregular in attendance at services ever since Panda was born, but Rosalind had assured him that when Panda was weaned, she would probably resume her old routine.

When he returned to his quarters in the rectory after Evensong, he saw that the basket was empty. Although he called and called, Faith did not come. "I wonder," he said to himself.

Down into the cellar he went, to the gap in the stacks of music. There were Faith and Panda, curled up in the small space between the music stacks. "Faith, it's cold and dusty down here. Now you come on back upstairs where it is bright and warm." Once again Henry picked up the kitten and carried her back upstairs with Faith accompanying him, mewing plaintively.

When Henry woke the next morning, the basket was empty again. "Now you listen to me, Faith," he said to the cat when he found them again in the basement.

"This has gone on long enough. A basement is a dreary place and dusty and dirty and not a fitting place for your son to grow up. You have a nice bed on the top floor, and I expect you to stop this dragging him around. I don't know what is the matter with you. Nobody is going to hurt you or Panda upstairs."

Back upstairs they went once more, but by early afternoon the basket was empty.

Henry went down to the kitchen where Rosalind, Ruth and Mabel were having scones and tea. He told them about Faith.

"Cats have a kind of special sense," Rosalind told him. "She must sense the war in the air. Perhaps she feels Panda is in danger. I think you'd better leave her down in the basement until she decides on her own to bring him back upstairs. "

"How could a cat know about the war? What harm could come to Panda? The church is strong and well built."

"If she is determined to take him down into the cellar, I think you should let her do it," said Rosalind, and the other two nodded their heads. "She will bring him back up when she is ready. I think we'd better take her basket down there if she's going to stay. She has been sleeping on that stone floor, and it has to be cold and damp and not good for either of them."

Henry shrugged his shoulders. "You know more about cats than I do. You win."

Rosalind patted his hand. "Just leave it to us."

The women took the basket and the litter box down to the basement and cleared out a larger space between the music stacks. All the while they worked, Faith sat watching them, and when they were finished, she dropped Panda into the basket and climbed in with him. Then she began to purr.

Bombs!

The very next night, Saturday, September 7, air raid sirens again set up their wailing. Henry felt safe in the church and remained in the rectory, but he turned out all the lights and sat looking out the window. Soon he heard the foreboding buzz of hundreds of bombers flying over the city. First the German planes dropped flares, lighting up the city, even Watling Street. Searchlights pierced the sky from the ground defenses, but they paled into nothingness in the brilliance of the flares. Then Henry heard bombs dropping a few streets away with great whistling sounds, followed by explosions. Flight after flight of bombers came across the city, dropping bombs and shrapnel. No planes flew directly over Watling Street, and Henry finally went to bed about midnight. When he heard the "All clear" siren, he looked at his watch: 4:00 a. m. He went back to sleep.

Next morning over their coffee he and Thomas listened to the morning radio news program. Hundreds of homes had been leveled and 448 men, women, and children in the city had been killed.

Henry held services the next day, but not many parishioners attended.

On Monday, September 9, he had to go to Westminster on business. He rode on his bicycle and had just started for home when the air raid siren went off; he popped into an air raid shelter for the night. Hundreds of German planes again flew over the city, dropping their deadly loads. As soon as it was light the next morning, Henry left the bomb shelter and hurried to a corner store where a radio was tuned to the morning news.

"During the night in London 417 civilians were killed by bombs," the radio newsman reported, "50 in one block of flats alone. Scores of non-military buildings and apartments were bombed, including eight churches."

"Eight churches!" Henry cried. "Horrible. Pray God not St. Augustine's!"

He dashed out of the store. His knees shook as he mounted his bicycle and set out at once for Watling

Street, steering around craters where bombs had hit and skirting crowds of spectators. Soon the street became impassable with rubble and wood splinters and piles of shattered window glass everywhere, and pieces of stone and bricks. He dismounted and walked the rest of the way, guiding his bicycle over hillocks of wreckage. "Pray God St. Augustine's was spared," he said aloud as he turned into Watling Street.

But Watling Street was one great mass of wreckage.

When he came to the church, tears filled his eyes and he sobbed. He stood in the street, aghast. Bricks lay everywhere and shards of what had been stained glass windows lay twisted and shattered. The nave of the church was gone. The tower still stood but the front wall was torn away, and half the roof arched overhead supported only by two walls. Flames leaped up from broken timbers all over the wreckage, and the heat made his face feel blistered.

Firemen played hoses on the wreckage. One of them saw Henry and motioned for him to step back. Henry climbed over piles of foundation stones and bricks until he could talk to the man. "Get away from here," said the fireman. "This roof is likely to crash any moment."

"I'm the rector of St. Augustine's," Henry said.

"Then you can help us. Has anybody been staying in the church overnight? We need to search through the rubble for any victims."

"Nobody except Faith and Panda and me. And I had gone to Westminster last night."

"Who are Faith and Panda?"

"My cat and her little son. They were in the basement. I have come to find them."

The firemen looked at the smoking ruins. "I'm afraid you have lost your cats," he said kindly. "No people or animals, either, could have lived through this. I'm sorry, sir. Step back now out of danger and let us get on with our work."

Henry stood looking at the heaps of ruins. He could see where the stairway had been, and he believed that somewhere down under the sagging floor Faith and Panda were there and alive.

The firemen left to answer an emergency somewhere else.

Henry began climbing over smoking timbers towards the corner where he thought Faith and Panda might be.

"Faith!" he called as loudly as he could. "Faith!"

He stopped to listen. All he could hear was the sound of fire engine sirens in another street.

"Faith! Faith!"

He climbed over a smoking timber. "Faith?"

He thought he heard her answer.

He climbed over a pile of flickering wreckage. "Faith?"

"Meow."

"Oh, God be thanked. I hear her."

With his bare hands he tore at the smoking timbers.

"I'm coming, Faith! I'm coming."

As he worked, Henry kept an eye on the sagging roof above them.

He kept calling. "I'm coming, Faith. I'll get you out."

Standing on a pile of wreckage, he saw several stacks of music, smoldering around the edges. He tossed pieces of the smoking sheets over his shoulder. "She's right around here, I know."

Suddenly there she was, crouched in the gap of music stacks, now beginning to burn around the edges.

Henry pulled her out, and under where Faith had protected him with her body, lay Panda.

"Oh, Faith!" Henry cried and the tears made tracks down his smoky face. He reached in and picked up the two sooty and frightened cats.

Part of the entry of the church was still standing, and Henry took the cats there. When he set them down on the floor, Faith looked up at Henry as if to say, "Where have you been so long? Why didn't you come sooner?"

Five minutes after Henry rescued the cats, the roof caved in with a fountain of sparks flying into the air. The spot where Faith and Panda had spent the night disappeared in the wreckage. Carrying the cats, Henry walked over the wreckage to the tower, which was still standing. He shut them in the vestry.

Henry stood in the street and watched the destruction of his church. After a while Thomas and Rosalind arrived, anxious expressions on their faces. They both began to weep as they looked at the ashes of their church.

"There is one thing to be thankful for," said Henry. "Faith and Panda are alive. If they had been up in the rectory, they would be dead."

"That cat knew more than we did," said Rosalind. "She sensed what was coming."

"I thank the Lord," said Henry.

"You certainly can't stay here," said Thomas. "Bring the cats and come home with us. Luckily our house is still standing, although many of the houses on our street are gone."

"That's very kind of you," replied Henry. "And I will come. I put the cats in the tower. It doesn't seem to be harmed."

The Blitz continued, night after night. Henry took Faith and Panda with him every day to the church tower, working to make it livable. "I will never leave you again, Faith," he told her.

On September 11 the bombers began coming over from the continent in the afternoons as well as at night. On September 15 two bombs fell on Buckingham Palace, but they failed to explode. After that the bombers came less frequently and finally stopped altogether.

The tower withstood the bombing, and parishioners came with mops and buckets and washed the walls, the floors and all the furniture. By the first of November, they were able to resume services in the tower.

Henry, Faith and Panda lived in the tower, and when Panda grew up, he went to stay in a nursing home where he soon became the pet of all the residents. Faith continued to attend church and lie at Henry's feet in the pulpit while he preached.

Henry asked a friend to take Faith's photograph. He had it framed and hung it on the chapel wall. Underneath he put up this legend:

Our dear little church cat Faith, the bravest cat in the world.

On Monday September 9, 1940, she endured perils and horrors beyond the power of words to tell.

Shielding her kitten in a sort of recess in a spot she selected three days before the tragedy occurred, she sat through the whole frightful night of bombing and fire, guarding her little kitten.

The roof and masonry exploded. The whole house blazed. Four floors fell through in front of her and fire and water were all around her. Yet she stayed calm and steadfast and waited for help.

We rescued her in the early morning while the place was still burning, but by the grace of Almighty God, she and her kitten were not only saved, but unhurt. God be thanked for his goodness and mercy to our dear little pet.

After Henry hung Faith's picture and the story of her bravery on the chapel wall, her story began to spread as people visiting the church told their friends about it.

Five years after the church was destroyed a woman named Maria Dickin heard Faith's story, and something wonderful happened.

Not for Faith

*M*aria Dickin was born in 1870 in a middle class London family. Her father was a Free Church minister. She was the oldest child of eight and when she grew up, she wanted to help out the family finances by working outside the home, something that just wasn't done in those days among families in her class.

She was determined to help her parents educate her younger brothers and sisters, and so after she finished her schooling, she opened a voice studio in Wimpole Street and taught singing and elocution for a number of years. When she was twenty-eight years old, she fell in love with a cousin, Arnold Dickin, and they were married. Arnold was a successful accountant and after their marriage, since her younger sisters and brothers had finished school or were being helped by the older ones, there was no longer any need for Maria to help support her parents. She gave up her studio and became a proper English housewife in their home at Hampstead Heath.

The leisurely life of supervising the household staff and attending teas and church jumble sales did not satisfy her, however, and she volunteered to go as a social worker in London's East End.

The East End was run down and dirty. As she went about into the homes of the poor residents, delivering food and clothing, she was appalled to see the conditions of their pets and work animals. She saw dogs and cats covered with mange eating out of gutters, crippled donkeys and horses pulling heavy loads of coal and produce and in backyards, pet goats and rabbits so thin that she could count their ribs under their skins.

At night over the dinner table she often described to Arnold the animals she had seen during the day. "In our social service work we hope to make the world a better place for people. I think that the animals deserve a better place to live, too."

Arnold nodded agreement.

Maria had a little Yorkie terrier named Andrew. One day when she called him to go for a walk, he tried to get up, but his back legs refused to work. "Andrew, what is wrong?" Maria picked him up and held him in her arms. The little dog whimpered and yipped. She put her cheek down to the top of his head, and sat down on a rocking chair, holding him in her arms. Andrew gave a sob of weariness and pain.

"I must take Andrew to the vet," she told Arnold. "Please bring the carriage around."

Maria told the vet how Andrew had sobbed. "It was almost like a human cry," she said.

The vet examined Andrew while Maria watched. At last he straightened up from the table where Andrew lay. "I am sorry to tell you that Andrew's legs are paralyzed and that he has severe kidney disease," he said.

"What can you do to help him?"

The doctor shook his head. "Mrs. Dickin, there is no medicine that will help Andrew. He is in great pain, and he will only get worse. The very kindest thing you can do for Andrew is to let me put an end to his suffering. I can give him a shot that will put him to sleep and he will never, never have pain any more."

Maria rose and went to the window, where she stood looking out for a long time. Then she turned to the vet and nodded.

She picked Andrew up and held him in her arms. "Dear, dear Andrew," she said softly to the dog, "you and I have been friends for many years. The doctor says you are in pain and cannot get better. I don't want you to suffer." She kissed the top of his head. "Give him the shot," she said. "I will hold him."

She arranged for Andrew to be buried in a pet cemetery. On the way home she said to Arnold, "I am so glad that I could afford to take Andrew to the vet and that I could help him out of this world without pain. But I think of the hundreds of animals of the poor who cannot afford a vet's bill for their sick pets. I must do something about it."

"What can you do?" asked Arnold.

"I am going to open a free dispensary in Whitechapel," Maria said. "People who cannot afford a vet may bring their animals to my dispensary for free treatment and medicine."

"That is a fine idea," said Arnold, "but who will pay for the dispensary?"

Maria's blue eyes sparkled. "You and I, to begin with. I will ask pharmaceutical companies for free medicines and vets to volunteer their services. I will ask my friends to contribute."

Arnold sighed. "Maria, Maria, I'm afraid you are in for trouble. But I will help you all I can. You find a room somewhere and I will pay the rent for a year. But you will probably have an uphill battle."

"You're a darling," said Maria and kissed him.

Arnold was right. When she asked for financial and professional help, doors slammed in her face. Many persons she approached told her that animals do not suffer pain — only human beings do. To them she said, "Have you ever suffered pain until you did not know how to bear it any longer? Animals suffer like that — only they are not able to say so."

She opened the People's Dispensary for Sick Animals in 1917, and in a short time she had to look for quarters large enough to accommodate 100 patients a day. She devised all sorts of ways to raise money.

By 1923 she found she had to incorporate, and at that time Arnold took over the task of fund raising.

The PDSA grew year after year, opening new clinics in cities throughout England and operating mobile units in rural areas and villages. Maria hired staff helpers and trained them herself, all financed by gifts from friends and animal lovers.

In 1937 the Royal College of Veterinary Surgeons
and the Department of Agriculture tried to force her to
close her clinics because she was giving away free what
their members depended on for their income. They also
suggested that animals were not receiving proper
treatment at her dispensaries.

Maria wrote to the directors, "If you are so
concerned about the proper treatment of the sick animals of the poor, open your own dispensaries; open
them everywhere. Show owners how to care for their
animals in sickness and in health. Do the same work as
we are doing. Instead of spending your time and energy
in hindering us, spend it in dealing with this mass
misery."

The college and the department dropped their
opposition, and the work continued.

During World War II many animals helped the
armed forces and civil defense groups. Pigeons carried
messages from troops, ships, and airplanes where radio
or telephones could not be used. Dogs located air raid
victims trapped under wreckage and rescued impris-
oned and buried pets. Horses of the Metropolitan Police
Force continued their work on London streets during the
bombardment of the city.

It was then that Maria established the Dickin
Medal to be awarded to any animal displaying conspicuous gallantry and devotion to duty to the armed forces
or civil defense.

The inscription on the bronze medal says
"PDSA" at the top, "For Gallantry" in the center and
"We Also Serve" at the bottom, all enclosed in a laurel
wreath. On the reverse side a citation for the recipient is
inscribed. The medal ribbon is green, dark brown and
pale blue, representing water, earth and air to symbolize
the navy, the army and civil defense and the air force.

Whenever a bird or animal was awarded a
Dickin Medal, the newspapers ran photographs and
stories about the awards. One day in January 1945
Rosalind saw a story about Beauty, a wire-haired terrier,
and her master Bill Barnet, a PDSA Veterinary Officer,
leader of one of the rescue squads during the bombing
of London.

After every bombing raid, Beauty and Bill
walked through the bombed areas in their district,
looking for animals trapped in the wreckage. One night
Bill and his squad members started digging in debris,
looking for trapped pets, when Bill noticed that Beauty

had gone off on her own and was digging in a spot across the street.

The squad turned up nothing where they had been digging, but when they pulled away the wreckage where Beauty was, they found buried under a splintered table a frightened cat.

After that all animal rescue squads took dogs with them and during the Blitz saved sixty-three pets that otherwise would have died in the ruins.

For her work Beauty was awarded the Dickin Medal.

Rosalind looked at Beauty's photograph in the paper.

She laid down the newspaper. "I have just had a brilliant idea," she announced. "This is probably the most brilliant idea I have ever had."

Ruth stood polishing a chalice. "My heavens! What is your idea?"

"This dog got her picture in the paper because she won a Dickin Medal." She pointed to Beauty's photograph. "I think that we ought to try to get a Dickin Medal for Faith. She did something a lot braver than this dog in the paper."

"You mean when she saved Panda?"

"That's right."

Both Ruth and Clara looked at the picture and story in the paper. "I think she should have one, too," Clara said.

"How can we get her one?" asked Ruth.

"I will write a letter to the PDSA and nominate her," said Rosalind, "and we will all sign it. You know, I think Faith knew the church was going to be bombed. Remember how Father Ross kept taking Panda back upstairs, but Faith took him right down again?"

"Maybe she didn't know the church was going to be bombed," said Clara, "but something certainly told her to move Panda. Extra-sensory perception. Cats have it. I read an article in the paper about it just the other day."

"They do," said Rosalind. "I read it, too. When the church was bombed, Faith probably could have saved herself. But she stayed with Panda."

"Should we ask Father Ross about it?" asked Ruth.

"I don't see why we need to bother him about it. Let's keep it a secret until we hear from the PDSA."

They agreed, and Rosalind sent off the letter to the PDSA describing Faith's heroism.

They could hardly wait until the answer came.

One morning several weeks later Clara picked up the post just after it came through the slot in the door. She rushed up the stairs two at a time and bolted into the room where Rosalind was watching Ruth polishing silver. She handed the letter to Rosalind. "It's from the PDSA! Oh, hurry up and open it!"

Rosalind slit the envelope and unfolded the paper.

Then her face lengthened. "Oh, dear!"

"What? What's the matter?"

"Faith can't have a Dickin Medal. She is not a member of the armed forces or the civil defense. She is a civilian cat, and civilians are not eligible."

Invitation

*T*hat's not fair," said Clara. "She is just as brave as any of those other animals."

Rosalind was still reading. "Cheer up," she said. "There's good news."

"Tell us! Tell us!"

"Mrs. Dickin was so impressed with Faith's bravery that she is going to have a special silver medal made for her, and she is going to come here to present it herself."

All three women whooped like schoolgirls. "Silver is better than bronze anyhow," said Ruth.

"Silver will go better with Faith's complexion than bronze," added Clara.

Henry, who had been working in the next room, heard the noise and stuck his head in the door. "What's going on?"

"Shall we tell him?" Rosalind asked the others.

"Oh, yes. Yes!"

They told him, and he was so excited he danced around the room with each of the women in turn.

"And she says she will present the medal herself? Let me see the letter."

After he read it, he handed it back to Rosalind. "Maria Dickin is a Commander of the British Empire. To think such a great lady would come here to present a medal to our dear little cat. How can we ever survive the excitement?"

"We'll manage," said Rosalind.

Next morning after Henry had gone to his study, Rosalind cleared her throat. "I have had another brilliant idea."

"You can hardly top the one you already have had," Ruth commented, opening the jar of silver polish. "But tell us."

"What would you think if we invited the Archbishop to come when Faith gets her medal?"

Ruth stared at Rosalind. "You mean the Arch-bishop of Canterbury?"

"Of course. Who else?"

"We wouldn't dare," said Clara, iron poised above a vestment she was pressing. "He wouldn't come anyhow."

"Why not? Faith is a church cat, and St. Augustine's is one of the Archbishop's parishes. We're always seeing his picture in the paper, visiting this church and that. We can invite him, anyhow. It's up to him whether he comes or not."

"I don't even know his name," said Ruth.

"You don't have to," Rosalind replied. "There is only one Archbishop of Canterbury. But it's Geoffrey Fisher. He lives in Lambeth Palace, just across the river. He could walk if he was of a mind to."

"How will we invite him? Give him a ring?"

"I'd be scared to ring the Archbishop on the telephone," said Clara. "Why, he's the head of the whole Anglican Church all over the world." She stood with the iron in midair.

"He doesn't scare me," said Rosalind. "I'll write to him. Before he was Archbishop, he was headmaster of a school and before that an ordinary priest like Father Ross or anybody else. I think he would feel honored to be invited to see Faith get her medal for bravery. We might even let him hold her while Mrs. Dickin puts the medal around her neck. Think what a wonderful picture that would make in the newspaper."

"Maybe you'd better ask Father Ross first," advised Ruth.

But Rosalind got paper and pen and wrote her letter without saying a word to Henry. When she went to address the envelope, however, she sat for a long time, thinking. "How do you address the Archbishop on an envelope?" she asked the other women. "It doesn't look right to say `Archbishop of Canterbury.' It looks so abrupt, like."

"Want me to ask Father Ross?" asked Ruth.

"Yes. But don't tell him what you want to know for."

Ruth bustled off on her errand and soon came hurrying back. "You write `The Most Rev. and Rt. Hon. Geoffrey Fisher,'" she reported. "You don't even say `Archbishop of Canterbury'."

"For heaven's sake. I'm glad we asked. Did Father Ross ask why you wanted to know?"

"Yes, but I pretended not to hear him."

Three days later the telephone rang in Henry's office.

"St. Augustine and St. Faith," Thomas said into the receiver.

"This is His Grace's secretary at Lambeth Palace," said a man's voice. "I'd like to speak to Mrs. Evans, please."

Thomas almost dropped the ear piece. "Certainly. Just a moment." He put his hand over the mouthpiece of the candlestick telephone. "His Grace's secretary wants to speak to Rosalind," he said to Henry across the desk.

Henry's eyebrows rose. "Whatever for, do you suppose?"

"With my wife Rosalind, you never can tell."

"I'll get her."

Henry ran to the altar guild room. "You're wanted on the telephone," he told Rosalind. "His Grace's secretary. Hurry."

She set down her teacup. She followed Henry into his office and picked up the telephone. "This is Rosalind Evans." She listened and a smile lit up her face. "Oh, that is splendid."

Henry and Thomas sat watching.

"Yes, at eleven o'clock, October 12. At St. Augustine's. Watling Street. Thank you very much."

She hung the ear piece on the hook.

"The Archbishop is coming to the ceremony," she said to Henry. "I must call the newspapers."

Henry sat as if a brick had fallen on his head. "I don't understand," he said finally. "How did the Archbishop know about it?"

"We invited him."

Henry stood up and walked over to the hearth where Faith lay sleeping. He picked her up. "Faith, did you hear that? The Archbishop of Canterbury is coming to see you get your medal from Mrs. Dickin. You are the bravest, most wonderful cat in the whole world. I think you should have a special treat."

He reached into his pocket and took out one of the treats Clara baked for Henry to give Faith at Eucharist. She took it gently out of his cupped fingers and chewed it enthusiastically.

A Special Honor

October 12, 1945 was a rare sunny day in London.

Watling Street had never seen such excitement. Laughing, chatting parishioners carrying trays and casseroles for the luncheon afterwards arrived long before eleven o'clock. Rosalind, Ruth and Clara had set the tables the day before and were on hand in the hall to arrange the food, which was to be served buffet style. The chapel was soon filled and some members had to bring in folding chairs from the parish hall.

Three newspaper reporters and three photographers stood outside the church.

Henry and Thomas went outside to wait. Henry carried Faith, who looked around at the scene with great interest.

At five minutes before eleven a long black limousine drew up to the curb in front of the church. Immediately the sexton inside the tower began ringing the church bells.

As the sounds of the bells quavered in the air, out of the car stepped the Archbishop of Canterbury. He was a man in his sixties with spectacles, a bald head and a fringe of gray over his ears. He wore a black suit with his clerical collar and purple Rabat. His vestments lay folded on the back seat of the car.

Henry and Thomas stepped forward. The Archbishop stepped around the car to the pavement and put his finger under Faith's chin and smiled. "And is this our dear little Faith?" he asked. The Archbishop's voice could easily be heard above the bells.

"This is Faith, Your Grace," said Henry proudly. "You have honored us with your presence today."

"I am glad to be here." He stroked Faith's head. "I like cats."

At that moment another black limousine slid silently up to the curb and the driver came around and opened the door. Maria Dickin stepped out. She was a tall woman, seventy-five years old, but slim and straight. She had a beautiful face with deep blue eyes, an imposing nose and smiling lips. She wore a black hat and coat, very smart.

There was handshaking all around. "The presentation will be in the chapel," said Henry. The Archbishop put on his vestments. Then he and Henry, carrying Faith, walked into the chapel first, followed by Thomas and Mrs. Dickin. Paul Maguire played "All Things Bright and Beautiful," and the congregation sang. Their voices sounded light and happy.

> "All things bright and beautiful,
> all creatures great and small,
> all things wise and wonderful,
> the Lord God made them all.
> Each little flower that opens,
> Each little bird that sings,
> he made their glowing colors,
> he made their tiny wings."

Henry put Faith down on the floor and walked to the altar. Faith went right along, as she always did, and sat down at his feet, looking up at him.

"The Lord be with you," said Henry.

"And with thy spirit," the congregation answered.

"Let us pray."

Henry read the collect for October 12: "Lord, we pray thee that thy grace may always precede and follow us, and make us continually to be given to all good works; through Jesus Christ our Lord, who liveth and reigneth with thee and the Holy Spirit, one God, now and forever. Amen."

Everybody sat down. "This is a very special and joyful occasion," said Henry. "Mrs. Maria Dickin, founder of the Peoples Dispensary for Sick Animals, has come to award a special medal for our dear little Faith, and the Archbishop of Canterbury Geoffrey Fisher has come to be with us today. Mrs. Dickin will present the award to Faith, after which the Archbishop will speak. Mrs. Dickin?"

Maria came forward with a large scroll of parchment in her hand. Henry bent down and picked up Faith. The Archbishop also came forward. "Would you like to hold Faith for the presentation, Your Grace?" asked Henry.

"I would be delighted."

Henry put Faith into the Archbishop's arms.

"We have gathered here today," Mrs. Dickin said, "to present a very special honor to a cat for extraordinary heroism. I know that you all have heard the story of how this little mother saved her son from the bombs during the Blitz. The PDSA wishes to honor her heroism with a special medal that has been cast for her. I will read the citation."

She took out of an envelope a large sheet of parchment and showed it to the people. On the citation was a sketch of a knight in armor on horseback. He held a banner which streamed across the top of the page. She read:

"Presented to Faith of St. Augustine's, Watling Street, E. C. for steadfast courage in the Battle of Britain, September 9th, 1940. Maria Dickin for the PDSA, October 12, 1945."

Maria held up the silver medal for everyone to see. "I will read the inscription," she said. "On the front it says `From the PDSA to FAITH, of St. Augustine's. Watling Street, E. C.'"

She turned the medal over and held it up.

"On this side it says `For steadfast courage in the Battle of London September 9, 1940.' I will now present the medal."

She looped the medal around Faith's neck and taking her face in her hands, she kissed her. Everybody stood up and applauded and smiled.

Mrs. Dickin went back to her seat. The Archbishop handed Faith to Henry and went to the pulpit. "The animals of God's creation inhabit the skies, the earth, and the seas," he said, glancing now and then at a book he had brought. "They share in the fortunes of human existence and have a great part in human life."

Faith, comfortable in Henry's arms, looked at the Archbishop with great round eyes as if she understood every word.

"Animals were saved from the flood," the Archbishop continued, "and afterwards made a part of the convenant with Noah. The paschal lamb brings to mind the Passover sacrifice and deliverance from the bondage of Egypt. A great giant fish saved Jonah; ravens brought bread to Elijah. And animals share in the redemption of all God's creation. We therefore invoke the divine blessing on this cat Faith. As we do so let us praise the Creator and thank him for setting us over other creatures of the earth." He bent and made the sign of the cross with his thumb on Faith's forehead.

"May God, who created the animals of the earth as a help to us, continue to protect and sustain us with the grace his blessing brings, now and forever. Amen."

After the presentation, Henry carried Faith into the church, Thomas escorted Mrs. Dickin and the Archbishop into the parish hall and everybody trooped after them. They feasted on chicken and ham, which everybody had pooled their ration stamps for, and on scalloped potatoes, creamed broccoli, buttered peas and carrots, cole slaw, strawberry jam, scones and whipped cream. Faith had a plate of fish at the table between Henry and Mrs. Dickin.

Next day Faith's photograph was in all the papers with Mrs. Dickin and the Archbishop, and a photographer from the *Sunday Dispatch* took Faith's picture looking at the citation. On Sunday the picture appeared in the newspaper under the headline "First Cat to Win a Medal for Courage." That day there was standing room only at the church.

Soon Faith's fame spread far beyond Watling Street. One day an American visiting in London saw Faith and the inscription and medal and when he went home, he told the humane society in his home town about it.

Not long afterwards the Greenwich Village Humane Society of New York sent Faith another silver medal and a citation. The story appeared in the New York and London newspapers.

As for Faith herself, the honors did not affect her in the least. She went about her duties in the church catching mice and serving as a good example in attending services regularly.

An English artist painted her portrait, and her photograph along with her story appeared in a book called *They Also Serve* by Hilary St. Hill Bourne. Extracts from the book along with Faith's photograph appeared in *The Johannesburg Sunday Times*.

Dear Little Church Cat

On September 28, 1948, Faith got up as usual when Henry did and followed him to the church kitchen. It was a typical morning: he and Thomas Evans enjoyed their morning coffee, and Faith had her breakfast. She ate a good breakfast, and afterwards she washed herself all over. Later she walked into the room where Henry was working at his desk and lay down in front of the warm fire. She stretched out her full length on a small Persian rug Henry had bought for her and lay staring into the leaping flames. Henry worked for an hour and finally put down his pen. He glanced at Faith. She had not moved since she first lay down. That was unusual, for she frequently stood up, stretched and turned around.

He walked over and knelt down to stroke her. Usually she gave a little chirp when he petted her, even though she was asleep. But no sound came from her. He put his ear to her chest. She was not purring.

Alarmed, he picked her up. Her eyes were open, but they stared at him without seeing him. "Faith! Faith!" He shook her lightly.

Faith did not rouse. Without a sound, lying before the fire which she loved and near her beloved Henry, Faith had slipped away from life. "Oh, Faith!" he exclaimed and buried his face in her fur. He sobbed.

Tears covered his cheeks as he carried her into the altar guild room. Ruth, Rosalind, and Clara gathered around him and in a moment they were all crying.

"Find a suitable box in the storeroom," Henry told Thomas. "If we don't have one, go to the pet shop and buy one."

Thomas brought a wooden box from the storage room. The women lined it with the Persian carpet. Henry laid Faith in the box and Thomas nailed it shut.

"We will bury Faith in the churchyard near the gate," said Henry. "Thomas, please ask the sexton to have the grave ready for tomorrow."

He posted a notice on the church door:

**Our dear little Faith passed away peacefully
September 28, 1948 at 10:30 a.m. after a happy life of
fourteen years.
Services will be held tomorrow at 10:30 a.m.
in the chapel.
Henry Ross, Rector**

Ruth's mouth fell open when she read the
notice. "A church service for a cat?" she said to Clara as
they stood on the front steps. "Did you ever hear of such
a thing?"

"No, I never did," Clara answered. "But there
never was a cat like Faith. Why shouldn't she have
services? After all, she attended this church for 14 years.
Let's go in and get on the telephone and let people
know."

"Do you suppose he will have the organ and
scriptures and everything?"

"Probably."

The word spread quickly once the three women
got on the telephones, and the next day by 10:15 the
church was filled.

Promptly at 10:25 Paul Maguire slipped onto the
organist's bench and played a Bach fugue. Faith had

always liked Bach. Then the choir boys in the red robes
and white fluted collars came up the aisle singing the
hymn by St. Francis of Assisi, patron saint of all animals:

> "All creatures of our God and King,
> lift up your voices, let us sing:
> Alleluia, alleluia!
> Bright burning sun with golden beams,
> pale silver moon that gently gleams:
> O, praise him, O praise him,
> Alleluia, alleluia, alleluia."

On the second verse, an altar boy holding aloft a
gold cross started up the aisle. Following him came
Thomas and then Henry, with the little box, covered by a
white pall, in his arms, singing in his strong tenor voice,

> "Great rushing winds and breezes soft,
> you clouds that ride the heavens aloft,
> O praise him, alleluia!
> Fair rising morn, with praise rejoice,
> stars nightly shining, find a voice,
> O praise him, O praise him,
> Alleluia, alleluia, alleluia."

Rosalind, standing with Ruth and Clara, joined
in the hymn, tears in her eyes.

> "And even you, most gentle death,
> waiting to hush our final breath,
> O praise him, alleluia!
> You lead back home the child of God,
> for Christ, our Lord, that way has trod:
> O praise him, O praise him.
> Alleluia, alleluia, alleluia.

The music as the hymn ended filled the aisles
and rose to the lofty ceiling of the tower as the choir
boys took their seats, and Henry set the little box on a
special stand beside the pulpit in the place where Faith
had always sat when Henry preached.

> "Let all things their creator bless,
> and worship him in humbleness,
> O praise him, alleluia!
> Praise God the Father, God the Son,
> and praise the Spirit, three in One:
> O praise him, O praise him,
> Alleluia, alleluia, alleluia."

"The service is from the Blessing of the Animals," Henry announced.

Rosalind read from Isaiah 11: 6-7. "And the wolf shall dwell with the lamb, and the leopard shall lie down with the kid, and the calf and the young lion and the fatling together; and a little child shall lead them. And the cow and the bear shall feed; their young ones shall lie down together; and the lion shall eat straw like the ox."

Thomas read from Psalm 8:
"Thou makest him to have dominion over the
    works of thy hands,
All sheep and oxen,
Yea, and the beasts of the field,
The birds of the heavens, and the fish of the sea,
Whatsoever passeth through the paths of the
    sea."

Henry stood behind the little box. "We have come today to celebrate the life of our dear Faith," he said, "who lived with us for fourteen years. She was a patient, kind, devoted cat, who loved her home here in

St. Augustine's. She was an exemplary mother to her little son Panda.

"In all her life Faith never raised her voice in anger nor did she complain if things didn't go her way, except for the time I tried to make her leave Panda on the third floor when she kept moving him to the basement.

"She was cared for devotedly and tenderly by all the members of this church, and particularly by Thomas, Rosalind, Ruth and Clara. It is our hope that somewhere in his beautiful and happy kingdom, God has already welcomed the brave little creature that he made. It can't be wrong of me to hope so, seeing that Jesus himself has told us `Not a sparrow falls to the ground but your heavenly father knows it.'

"It is in this that I rejoice and put my trust for our dear little friend Faith."

He bent over and placed a kiss on the little box, and there wasn't a dry eye in the church.

He gave Thomas a signal, and the verger picked up the box. Paul Maguire put his hands on the keyboard and the joyous sounds of "Hallelujah" from *Messiah*, shook the air. The choir boys led the way to the churchyard, followed by Thomas with the box and Henry and all the parishioners.

Henry placed the box in the grave. Then he read from his prayer book, "O God, whose blessed Son was laid in a sepulcher in the garden: Bless, we pray, this grave, and grant that she whose body is to be buried here may dwell with Christ in paradise, and may come to thy heavenly kingdom; through thy son Jesus Christ our Lord. Amen."

Thomas began to shovel the earth into the grave. "In sure and certain hope of the resurrection to eternal life through our Lord Jesus Christ," Henry read from his book, "we commend to Almighty God our sister Faith, and we commit her body to the ground, earth to earth, ashes to ashes, dust to dust. The Lord bless her and keep her, the Lord make his face to shine upon her and be gracious unto her, the Lord lift up his countenance upon her and give her peace. Amen."

Henry closed the book and walked sorrowfully back into the church. Slowly the others left the church yard.

Newspapers on four continents carried news of Faith's death the next day. Headlines spoke of her as

"Bravest Cat in the World" and "Cat Heroine of London Bombing." Stories appeared in newspapers in England, in the United States, in South Africa, and in Australia. All the stories retold the tale of her night of terror while the bombs fell around and over her, and how she remained by her little son, protecting him with her body.

Stirred by Faith's death, a Church of England clergyman at Hereford held in her honor a blessing of the animals service. The next Sunday Rev. L. B. J. Snell invited the children of his parish to bring their animals to church. Ducks, chickens, cats, dogs, guinea pigs, a goldfish, a lamb and a mouse named Angela turned up at the church while twenty horses waited outside. "Animals and birds are part of God's creation," said Vicar Snell. "There are animals and birds in Heaven as well as human beings and angels."

Some of the parishioners wanted to get another cat for the rector, but Henry said no. Many a sunny afternoon afterwards he spent with his book, sitting by the little grave in the churchyard. "Never another cat for me," he said. "Dear little Faith."

The time came and not too long after that when St. Augustine's church was closed and Henry retired. He took Faith's medals with him when he left the church for the last time.

Today the boys of St. Paul's choir school hold classes in the tower.

And under the grass where happy boys run and play, sleeps Faith, the dear little church cat, the bravest cat in all the world.

Part Two

✦

Simon: Terror of the Rats

Up Anchor!

April 1949

*A*lmost a year after Faith died, on the other side of the world, on a ship in the Yangtze River, lived a small black and white cat named Simon.

Simon stretched out on the desk of Captain Bernard Skinner, watching the tip of the captain's pen leave a track of blue ink on the paper.

In the light of the captain's reading lamp, Simon's fur shone. He was a green-eyed, black cat with a lop-sided white blaze to the right of his nose, white cheeks and chin, a white bib and paws.

He uncurled a paw from under his chest and swiped at the moving pen. The captain, a middle-aged man with face browned from many years at sea, nudged the paw away, and Simon folded it again under his chest.

Bernard Skinner was captain of His Majesty's Ship *Amethyst*, a 300-foot frigate of the Royal Navy, which lay at anchor at Kiangyin, on the muddy Yangtze River, 100 miles upriver from where it emptied into the East China Sea.

It was April 20, 1949, a hot, steamy day on the river.

Captain Skinner had anchored at Kiangyin on the advice of his two Chinese river pilots to wait for daylight before sailing farther up the dangerous river. The Yangtze with its soft bottom of mud and sand and subject to seasonal floods and typhoons often changes course and is dangerous to navigate in the daytime, let alone at night. What was more, the Nationalists, then in control of the river, had forbidden all night traffic.

More than a year before, Simon had been playing with an empty spool in the armaments supply store in Hong Kong, where he had been born two years before. The captain of the *Amethyst* came in to pick up supplies.

"You'll need a mouser for the ship," the clerk said, scooping the kitten off the floor. "This fellow is just the right one. His name is Simon. Comes from a long line of ship's cats."

All sea-faring ships need cats. Mice and rats love to live on ships, creeping in on hawser cables, jumping aboard from docks, coming in along with freight shipments.

Mice and rats damage ships, raiding the food storage areas and chewing fabrics to make nests for their young. They also carry viruses, which can be passed on to crew and passengers by mosquitoes or fleas that have bitten infected rodents and then bite a person. A cat on a ship is better than 100 rat traps.

The captain took the kitten in his arms and looked into his light green eyes. Simon looked steadily back into the gray eyes of the captain.

"He will do fine," he said. "Can you make him a name tag?"

"Of course." The clerk etched "SIMON" and "HMS *Amethyst*" on a metal tag and fastened it to a red leather collar. Simon, eight months old, wearing his collar, came on board the *Amethyst*, riding on the captain's shoulder.

Now Simon watched the scrolling pen as the captain continued writing a letter to his wife at home in England. "I'll mail this when we get to Nanking to-night," he wrote. "We sail as soon as it is light enough."

The letter would never be finished.

Captain Skinner looked at his watch and put down his pen. He scratched Simon on the back of his head.

It was 5:10 a.m. The captain was up early to get his ship to Nanking before the truce between the Chinese Communists and the Nationalists expired.

Simon was up early because whenever the captain got up, Simon did, too.

The Chinese Communists, fighting to overthrow the Chinese Nationalist government, had established troops on the north side of the river, facing the Nationalists on the south side.

The Communists, who were winning, had called a truce and given the Nationalists until midnight to accept their terms for ending the war. If the Nationalists did not accept, the fighting would begin again.

Vice Admiral Sir Alexander Madden, assistant head of the British Far East Command, stationed at Hong Kong, had ordered *Amethyst* to cruise up the

Yangtze to Nanking to relieve the frigate *Consort*, which
had been guarding the British Embassy there for several
months. If the Communists captured Nanking, the
British in the city would have to be evacuated. The truce
would last until midnight, plenty of time for *Amethyst* to
reach Nanking and for *Consort* to sail downstream to
safety at Shanghai.

Captain Skinner gave Simon a pat on the rump
and left the cabin. Simon climbed after him up the
ladder to the bridge. The captain flipped the intercom
switch with his thumb.

"Men of the *Amethyst*," he said, "in one minute
we will start on our journey up the river. As you know,
we are entering a war zone. His Majesty's government
has not taken sides in this war, and we expect no trouble
from either side. We will fly the white ensign, however,
and carry furled Union Jacks on the sides of the ship to
identify us. God bless us as we sail. And now, start
engines, up anchor!"

At the order the engines roared and the chains
holding the anchor creaked as the lifting mechanism
turned. The ship moved forward in the brown water and
left a foamy wake spreading out behind her.

Simon rubbed his side against the captain's leg and left the bridge. Down the ladder to the foredeck he went, his nose testing the air as he walked, ears twisting this way and that. He walked past the tantalizing smells from the petty officers' mess, the stewards' mess, the stokers' mess, the seamen's mess, all places where he sometimes picked up tidbits of food from the men. All were empty now. He walked on, listening for squeaks of mice and rats in the rigging.

As the ship, its engines pulsing, slipped through the water, the cat plodded down to the engine room and back up to the galley. Crew members he passed spoke to him, and he returned the greeting with a small "Meow."

Inside the galley Petty Officer George Griffiths had unwrapped a joint of beef for the noon lunch. As he stood sharpening his knife, he felt a soft brushing against his leg. He glanced down.

"Simon, what are you doing up at this hour?" he asked. "Cooks and such have to get up at five o'clock, but cats don't have to." Simon stared up at him, bright eyes pleading.

Griffiths grinned and shook his head. "It's not time for your breakfast yet. Go back to your bunk."

Simon did not move. He kept looking at Griffiths and making little silent meows.

"Oh, all right, since you're here. But you'll be pestering me for another breakfast at the regular time."

He opened the refrigerator door. Simon poked his nose inside as he always did, standing as if he were a scholar studying an encyclopedia. Griffiths took out a small package and a bottle of milk. As the door swung to, Simon backed up and followed Griffiths to the counter, hopping up on it in one spectacular leap and sniffing delicately at the package. "It's minced chicken and porridge for you this morning." The cook took a white china bowl from a shelf and turned out the contents of the package into it. He set it on the floor. "There you are, I'll fix the porridge."

Simon was a mannerly eater. He did not finish the contents of the bowl all at one time, but halfway through, he walked away, sat down and looked at Griffiths as if he were about to comment on the weather. Then he went back to the bowl and finished the chicken, polishing the china surface with his pink tongue until the bowl looked as if it had just come out of the dishwasher. He waited patiently for the porridge.

While Simon sat at the porridge bowl, Griffiths cut shallow nicks in the joint of beef with the tip of his knife and inserted slivers of garlic. When the porridge had vanished, Simon walked to the galley door, where he stood for a time opening and shutting his mouth and running his pink tongue around the edges to take up any stray bits of porridge or milk. Then he sat down and licked his right paw and used it to wash the right side of his face, even behind his ear. When that side was clean enough to satisfy him, he did the left side. He cleaned the insides of his hind legs and polished his snowy chest with his tongue.

He stepped out of the galley and trotted along the deck back to the cabin he shared with the captain.

Captain Skinner had returned from the bridge. His officer's white hat lay on its crown on the table. Simon stepped into the hat, curled himself into a circle inside it and half closed his eyes.

Attack

$\mathcal{A}$t eight o'clock the captain spoke again into the intercom. "All hands at stations."

From below decks came the noise of 183 crew members, many of them teen-age boys on their first voyage, scurrying to their assigned stations.

Captain Skinner arrived on the bridge at 8:20, scanning the shores through his binoculars. Simon followed at 8:21. "At 8:30 we will be passing a Communist camp," the captain said to his fellow officers on the bridge. Although he looked carefully, he could see nothing but low-lying dark green shrubbery on the shore.

The ship had been sailing at eleven knots per hour. At 8:30 Captain Skinner spoke into the intercom. "Increase speed to sixteen knots."

Nine minutes later from behind the shrubs on the north shore puffs of smoke appeared.

Boom, boom, boom.

Explosions shook the air. Shells screeched over the ship. Some fell short of the ship and landed in the river, sending up spouts of brown water. Others whistled by overhead.

"Full ahead, both!" Captain Skinner shouted down the voice tube to the engine room. "Display Union Jacks!"

Giant red, white, and blue flags painted on canvas cascaded down the sides of the ship.

The ship surged forward.

Simon backed down the bridge ladder and bolted under the captain's bunk.

The shooting stopped as unexpectedly as it began. Captain Skinner hurried to the wireless room to send a report. He wrote:

HAVE BEEN FIRED ON FROM NORTH BANK AT BEAVER ISLAND BY MEDIUM ARTILLERY. TEN SINGLE GUN SALVOES AND SOME SMALL ARMS. SHIP WAS FLYING MASTHEAD ENSIGN AND UNION JACKS WERE SHOWN BOTH SIDES AFTER SALVO. NO HITS. FIRE WAS NOT RETURNED AS NO

DEFINITE TARGET COULD BE IDENTIFIED BECAUSE OF MIST.

He returned to the bridge and gave the message to the wireless officer to encode and send to Vice Admiral Madden. Simon came with him. Before the wireless officer could reach for his code book, a 75 mm. shell crashed into the ship four feet above the flag deck, punching a three-inch-diameter hole in the wheel house wall before exploding on the port side.

Another 75 mm. shell crashed into the bridge and exploded. Simon bolted for the ladder and backed down. When he almost reached the deck, an exploding piece of shrapnel pierced his leg and back.

Simon fell to the deck.

He began to crawl. A wall crashed in splinters in front of him. He pulled himself under a piece of lumber and lay motionless, unseeing and unhearing.

When Simon opened his eyes, he could see little chinks of light. He stretched out one paw and then the other and dragged himself toward the light. His back hurt and one back leg would not move well. He scrabbled with his front paws and inched on his belly and at last he poked his head into the light.

The ship was silent. The familiar beat of the engines had stopped. Piles of sticks and broken plaster lay everywhere.

He pulled himself free and sat up, looking first this way and then that.

He sniffed the air. A fragrance of food floated through the dusty air. He was hungry. He started for the galley, took a few steps, and flopped on the floor.

He struggled up and took a few more steps.

He saw in front of him a pair of black shoes.

"Griffiths!" a voice above him called. "There's a cat here!" Simon had never heard the voice before.

In a moment he was snatched up by a pair of strong arms that smelled familiar. Griffiths buried his nose in Simon's fur. "Simon, you 're alive. Son of a gun. I thought you were dead."

The first voice spoke again. "What's this cat doing aboard the ship?"

"He's the ship's cat, sir. Captain Skinner brought him aboard two years ago. He's been on many voyages with us. Best ratter in the King's Navy! He bunked in the captain's cabin. Very fond of Simon, was Captain Skinner."

"Well, he can't bunk with me," said the voice. "I don't like cats. You'll have to find him another place."

"Yes, sir."

Griffiths turned and carrying Simon, headed for the galley. He put him down on the counter. "Let's look at you, Simon. Why, your whiskers have been singed off. And look at this blood on your back and your leg. I think you caught some shrapnel." He set Simon on the galley counter and lifted a pinch of fur on Simon's back between his thumb and forefinger. "You're dehydrated. No wonder. You haven't had anything to eat or drink since we were hit five days ago. Oh, Simon, we are in a hell of a fix. The Communist guns knocked our ship out in five minutes. We went aground on a mud bank on Rose Island and only got off it yesterday morning. *Consort* came from Nanking to help us, but the Communists shelled them and drove them off. Nineteen of our crew were killed. Captain Skinner was killed. The ship is wrecked in the river."

He rubbed his eyes with his bare arm. "Well, it's no use me standing here telling you all this. You don't know what I'm saying anyhow. Let's get some water into you and then a little food."

He set a bowl of water in front of Simon, but the cat sat with his head drooping and made no effort to drink.

Griffiths walked to a first aid cupboard and took out a medicine dropper. He squeezed the bulb and filled the glass tube with water. Taking Simon's head in one hand, he held the dropper to a corner of his mouth and gently squeezed out a few drops of water. Simon swallowed.

"That's the brave boy! Here, have some more."

He again emptied the dropper into Simon's mouth.

"I have some minced chicken," Griffiths said. "Stay there until I get it."

Simon did not move from the spot on the counter. When Griffiths came back with a little minced chicken in the palm of his hand, Simon stretched out his pink tongue and took a lick of it and then a bite. And then another one. And another.

In a little while he sat up and looked up expectantly at Griffiths. "You want more, do you? I think we'd better wait a while till we see whether you keep that down. I'm going to take you to Dr. Fearnley. He's the ship's new doctor. Dr. Alderton got killed, too."

Griffiths picked Simon up and carried him to the sick bay where Dr. Michael Fearnley passed kind hands over his body. "He's got shrapnel wounds in four places," the doctor said, "and his face has been burned. His whiskers will grow back in, and I'll clean and stitch his wounds."

"Will he be all right?"

"I can't be sure, but I hope so. His heart is weak. Come back for him in an hour."

"Yes, sir."

Griffiths went to the captain's cabin to get Simon's bed and litter box. He cleared out a corner in the petty officers' mess for Simon.

When he went back to get Simon, the cat was sitting up, looking better although he had a number of shaved spots where the doctor had take out bits of shrapnel and stitched the lesions.

Griffiths took him to his new quarters and showed him his bunk, a wooden box lined with clean straw, and his litter box. "This is your new bunk," he told Simon. "Captain Kerans doesn't like cats. Now you take a nice snooze, and when you wake up, come down to the galley and I'll have dinner for you."

Simon watched Griffiths leave the mess hall. Then he hopped stiffly out of the box and walked out on the deck. As he started towards the aft deck, he heard a call go out over the voice pipes, and from every direction sailors came, heading the same direction he was going. Simon followed them.

On the deck lay the bodies of the men who had been killed in the shelling. Each body had been sewed into a hammock weighted with two live shells so that it would sink to the bottom of the river.

The ship's crew stood at attention while Captain Kerans read the Anglican service for the dead beginning "I am the resurrection and the life, saith the Lord: he that believeth in me, though he were dead, yet shall he live: and whosoever liveth and believeth in me shall never die."

He read Psalm 90 and led the men in the Lord's Prayer.

"We therefore commit his body to the deep," the captain continued, "looking for the resurrection of the body, and the life of the world to come through our Lord Jesus Christ." Captain Kerans then read out a name, the boatswain blew his whistle, and two crewmen lifted a hammock-wrapped body over the rail and let it slip into the water. Seventeen times the captain read a name, and a form sank into the river.

Then all the sailors put their hats back on and silently left the deck.

Simon limped after Griffiths back to the galley for another meal.

With his stomach full, he felt like taking a nap. He padded down the hallway towards the captain's cabin where he always took his afternoon nap. The door had been half blown away, and he walked in. Wreckage littered the floor.

The man in the black shoes sat at the chart table where Captain Skinner always worked, and Simon approached him silently. He sat down on his haunches and studied him.

The man at the chart table was not his old friend. He smelled different. He was a different shape, longer and slimmer. His voice sounded thinner and higher.

After watching him for a while, Simon tensed his muscles and leaped. But he was not strong enough to reach the table top. He grabbed with his front claws, but he slid back to the floor with a thump.

"What in the holy blazes —" exclaimed Captain Kerans. He looked down at Simon, who began to wash himself in embarrassment. "Who invited you in here?"

The new captain picked him up and pitched him out into the hallway. "Get out and stay out," he said. "I don't like cats."

Simon sat down outside the door and seemed to be thinking. This was not right. Perhaps if he went back in quietly, the stranger would not see him. He poked his head inside the door and slipped inside.

On noiseless feet Simon walked to the bunk, leaped to the chair at the foot of the bunk, and from there he jumped onto the soft bed. He lay down with the pillow at his back, wrapped his tail around him, and snuggled his chin into the pillow. He closed his eyes.

Captain Jack Kerans, who had been sent from Nanking to replace Captain Skinner, sat studying the charts of the river course to Nanking. About 6:00 p.m. Jack French brought him a radio message from Vice Admiral Madden in Hong Kong:

LATEST NEWS JUST RECEIVED BY TELE-PHONE FROM NANKING INDICATES THAT COM-MUNISTS HAVE CROSSED IN SOME STRENGTH FIFTEEN MILES EAST OF NANKING AND THE

SITUATION IS EXPECTED TO DETERIORATE RAP-
IDLY. YOU ARE THEREFORE NOT REPETITION NOT
TO PROCEED TO NANKING.

It looked to Kerans as if the ship would have to
stay where it was for some time. When he checked the
ship's condition and the supplies, he found she had 260
tons of fuel oil and sufficient food and water for two
months.

Able Seaman Simon

The weekend passed quietly. The anchored ship swung with the river current. The men aboard worked at repairing the shell damage and watched the river traffic of junks and sampans.

Lieutenant Stewart Hett came to the cabin on Tuesday afternoon, April 26. "Three soldiers on the north shore are hailing the ship and waving a paper, sir," he reported.

Captain Kerans threw down his pen and picked up his hat. "Damn that cat!" he shouted.

His steward, But Sai, had been waiting outside. "Yes, sir?" he called, dashing around the door frame.

"Cat hairs all over the insides of my hat! Here." Kerans tossed the hat to But Sai. "Brush it out. I'll skin that cat when I catch him."

"Simon always sleep inside Captain Skinner's hat."

"Well, I'm the captain now, and I don't want a cat sleeping inside my hat."

The captain, Hett, and But Sai walked to the starboard deck. Simon padded after them. But Sai called to the men, who shouted back. "They want to talk with someone in authority immediately," the steward translated. "Either on the ship or on shore."

"Very well," said the captain. "Lieutenant Hett, have the whaler brought around."

Captain Kerans picked up the intercom. "This is your captain. I need two volunteers who can swim and row and one petty officer to go ashore to talk with the Communists. Report to the foredeck."

He chose Petty Officer Henry Freeman because he was about the same size and weight as Lieutenant Hett. He ordered him to put on Hett's white uniform. "The Communists will feel better if they think they are talking with a senior officer," he explained.

Freeman and But Sai got into the boat along with two seamen, and Kerans and Simon watched them row ashore.

Hours later Simon followed Freeman to the captain's cabin. Kerans indicated a chair for Freeman, and Simon hopped up on Freeman's lap. "Why did you bring that cat in here?" Kerans asked.

"I didn't bring him. He just came." Freeman stroked Simon's coat gently. "You probably know Simon was Captain Skinner's cat, sir," he went on, "and he usually came to our conferences with the captain.

"I don't understand how a cat can be such a privileged character. Take him out of here."

"Yes, sir." Freeman carried Simon out and set him down on the deck.

"Make your report, please."

"The Chinese took us in a truck about twelve miles to a peasant's house. There we waited for about an hour. Then a Major Kung arrived. He began by saying that the whole incident was *Amethyst*'s fault because she fired the first shot. I very firmly made it plain that it was his artillery that fired the first shot, and that we only fired after we had been fired on.

"He contended again that he knew we were a British ship, but that since we fired first, we brought on all the trouble. I asked him if his forces would allow us safe passage down the river."

"What did he say to that?"

"He said he had no authority to grant such a request. Only the general in Nanking could grant us safe passage. He offered to provide a sampan for our use. Up to then I thought he didn't speak English. But then he said in English he regretted that our action in firing first had damaged the previous good relations between the British and the Chinese. Then he left. When we went back to the truck, it had disappeared. But Sai and I had to walk the twelve miles back to our boat on the river. That is why we were gone so long."

"I think he fired at us by mistake," said Kerans, "and now he is trying to cover up with his superiors by claiming we fired first."

The next day Chinese soldiers brought the sampan to the ship and again requested that Captain Kerans come for a further interview. This time Kerans sent young, ruddy-faced Lieutenant Hett.

The conference accomplished nothing. Again Kung accused *Amethyst* of firing the first shots, and Hett accused the Communists. Kung hinted that *Amethyst* might have to remain on the Yangtze until the Chinese civil war ended.

After the second unsatisfactory conference, life on the Yangtze settled into a dull, hot, humid procession of boring days of sweat and ship repair.

Day after day passed, and the days turned into weeks. Life on the ship became almost unbearable. The thermometer rose to 110 degrees Fahrenheit every day below decks. Simon smelled the sweat on the men's clothes. They discarded shirts and wore only shorts.

One day Dr. Fearnley saw Simon limping past the sick bay on his way to the hold to look for rats. "Why don't you come in here and visit these chaps?" he asked and held the door open. Simon walked inside where row on row of cots each held an injured lad.

"I'm going to try something," Dr. Fearnley told his attendant. He picked Simon up and carried him over to a bed in the corner where Seaman Mark Allen lay with his eyes closed. The boy, who was only sixteen, had lost both legs below the knee in the shelling and for four days since he had regained consciousness, he had refused to talk or eat or even open his eyes.

The doctor set Simon on the boy's bed. Simon sat looking at him, but the boy's eyes remained closed. The doctor moved Simon onto the boy's chest and placed the limp hand on the cat's back.

"Somebody's here to see you, Mark," said the doctor.

Mark opened his eyes just a little. When he saw Simon's steady gaze, he opened them further. The corners of his mouth quirked ever so slightly.

"I have a cat at home," he said. "But I'll never see him again." He pushed Simon away and turned his face into his pillow.

"Of course you will. He's waiting at home right now, looking for you. But you have got to eat and gain strength," Dr. Fearnley told him. "We're going to get you new legs that will work almost as well as the old ones. You'll be able to walk as well as before."

Mark put his hand up over his face.

The next day Dr. Fearnley took Simon to see Mark again and left him sitting on Mark's bed, while he went to the next patient in the sick bay. Simon crawled up on Mark's stomach and began kneading, as he often did before settling down. Mark opened his eyes. His thin hand reached out and stroked Simon's rough fur. The boy began to sob.

Dr. Fearnley hurried to him. "Cook's got some good vegetable soup in the galley. How would you like me to get you a bowl of it? Simon will stay here with you."

Mark nodded ever so slightly. He stroked Simon, who settled down by him and began purring.

From that day on Mark began to eat and gain strength. Simon visited every day. There was always a little treat for Simon on his tray.

By the time a month had passed, Mark was able to get around the ship in a wheelchair.

One day after a meeting in his office Captain Kerans walked with Hett to the door. Outside sat Simon. At his feet lay a dead rat.

"Good boy!" exclaimed Hett, stooping to rub Simon's back. "You're back at work, I see. Feeling better, are you?"

"Why do you pay any attention to that cat?"

"Simon is one of the rare pleasures on this miserable ship, sir. He visits the wounded every day and makes their life a little better. And if it weren't for Simon, Griffiths says, the rats would move into the galley and storerooms and ruin the food."

Kerans nudged the rat's body with the shining black toe of his shoe. "Why is this rat here?"

"It's a gift for you, sir."

"It's disgusting, "

"Not to Simon, sir. He is proud of killing the rat — that's his job. And he's making a gift of it to you."

Captain Kerans stood staring down at Simon. Simon looked right back at him, his face turned up, and gave a little meow. The captain bent over and reached out his hand. Simon sniffed at the fingers. The captain stroked Simon's back.

Hett grinned and picked the rat up by the tail. "I'll pitch this fellow overboard, sir. Would you mind distracting Simon while I do it, sir? Play with him a little or take him into the cabin."

"Why?"

"I don't want him to see me throw the rat overboard."

"For God's sakes, why?"

"Cats have feelings, just like people. He would feel bad if he thought you didn't like his present."

The Giant Killer

One morning in the galley Simon left his porridge bowl and limped to the counter. He stood on his hind legs, his two white forepaws resting on the cupboard under the counter.

George Griffiths, stirring a pot of lamb stew on the stove, looked around.

Before the shelling Simon had been able to jump to the counter top from a sitting start without any visible effort, but he had not yet regained his old strength. Griffiths lifted him to the counter.

Simon advanced toward a carton standing in a corner of the wall, his ears standing at alert, his tail switching back and forth. He made a little clicking sound.

"Don't tell me Mao Tse-tung is behind that carton!"

Griffiths had been complaining that the largest rat he had ever seen had been leading a pack in attacks on the stores in the galley. He had seen the leader once and named him for the Communist chief because he was so big. Although he had tried to trap him, the rat was so wily he took the bait every time but escaped. "I'll pull the carton away, Simon. Look out, now."

Griffiths edged the carton from the corner gingerly and sure enough in the corner crouched a black rat that looked almost as big as Simon. He had little rounded ears, a sharp nose, a black coat and a long, thin tail. He glared straight at Simon and stood motionless.

Simon crouched switching his tail back and forth, staring at the rat.

He reached out one paw and then the other and inched on his belly nearer the rat.

For several minutes, the terrorized rat sat frozen, powerless to move, the cat advancing inch by inch.

Suddenly Simon sprang. The rat leaped. Simon sank his sharp teeth into the rat's neck behind his ears, snapping his spinal cord.

The rat died at once.

"Good cat, Simon!" Griffiths shouted. "Hey," he called, sticking his head out of the galley, "Simon killed Mao Tse-tung! Come see!"

Several seamen stood at the deck rail, looking across the brown river to the mainland. They came in a hurry to see the rat.

"Biggest rat I ever saw," Griffiths exclaimed, holding it up by the tail. "Simon killed him one, two, three, just like that."

"Hip, hip, hurrah for Simon!" shouted a seaman, and the others joined in.

"I'm going to show this one to the captain," Griffiths went on. "He ought to give Simon a prize."

A week or so later Griffith's log showed Simon had killed rats in the stokers' mess, the potato locker, the portside galley, the bridge, the forward mess deck, the petty officers' pantry, the port passageway, and the aft and forward decks.   He killed an average of five rats a day.

One morning Captain Kerans asked Dr. Fearnley to come to his cabin. When he arrived, he was followed by Simon, who had just finished his breakfast.

"Something is wrong with me," said Kerans from his bunk. "I ache all over, and I can't get up."

"Let's have a look at you." Fearley listened to his heart and then looked into his eyes and ears. He listened to his lungs.

"There's nothing wrong with you that a few days' rest in bed won't cure you of," the doctor said.

"What's wrong with me?"

"Well, I'll call it fibrositis."

"What's that?"

"A kind of general complaint. It's caused by living so long in excessive heat and humidity. I'll give you some pills and you stay in bed for three days and you'll be as good as ever."

The captain groaned. "I haven't time to be sick." He slid down into bed. Simon made himself a nest next to the captain's back.

When he woke an hour later, Captain Kerans reached back to find out what was making the lump in the bed. His hand touched Simon's soft, thick fur. The captain turned over and looked at the sleeping cat. He was lying on his side with his chin turned up and the top of his head flat on the sheet. Kerans stroked his side, and Simon gave a little chirp without waking.

A soft look came into Kerans' eyes.

Typhoon

The crew began to look thin and pinched about their mouths as their energy deserted them. Only one sailor kept up his daily activities with spirit and good will: Able Seaman Simon. He patrolled the ship, visited the sick, killed mice and rats, and made life bearable for his fellow shipmates. He never complained about the heat or his health. Most of the ship's men were too busy with their assigned work to pay much attention to Simon.

Young Mark Allen, however, had nothing but time, while he was recuperating from his wounds. He noticed that Simon's coat was dull and rough looking, and he asked Dr. Fearnley for a hair brush. The next time Simon jumped up on Mark's bed, Mark showed him the brush and explained he was going to use it on his fur.

Simon scratched his chin on the brush. Then Mark
stroked his back ever so lightly with the brush. Simon
loved it. After that he came twice a day for a brushing,
and soon Simon's fur glistened. He looked quite handsome.

Admiral Sir Patrick Brind, who was Madden's
superior and Commander in Chief of the Far East
Command, became irritated with the situation on the
Yangtze. He decided to try to speed matters along by
negotiating with General Yuan, the Communist commander, using Captain Kerans to deliver messages
between them. On July 14 he sent a message to the crew
of the *Amethyst* which the captain read to the crew,
including Simon:

It is clear that the Communists have been
holding you hostage to wring admissions from the
British government which would not only be untrue but
would harm the cause of free nations in the future. For
the present, therefore, you are in the forefront of the cold
war in which the cause of freedom is being attacked. I
know it is a pretty hot war as far as you are concerned,
and your stand is widely recognized and greatly ad-
mired.

A shipment of medicines, soap, disinfectant, matches, cigarettes, and Chinese money was delivered by a Sunderland flying boat from Hong Kong, but nothing could ease the suffering from the extreme heat. On July 19 the temperature reached 110 degrees on the decks and 118 degrees in the engine room. Two days later Kerans was forced to have the ship's generators shut down every day from 6:00 a.m. until dark to conserve fuel. Even Simon walked the decks very slowly.

The next day at a meeting on shore, General Yuan told Kerans he would not consider Brind's proposal for negotiating the ship's release, repeating that until the British admitted their guilt for the damage they and the British rescue warships had caused in April, the ship would have to stay right where it was.

Life on board became even worse when Vice Admiral Madden radioed:

TYPHOON GLORIA EXPECTED TO HIT YANGTZE VALLEY SUNDAY NIGHT, JULY 24 AND 25.

The ship was anchored by two cables, but Kerans realized that if the cables did not hold, he would either have to try to take the ship downriver in the storm or else possibly lose her to the wind and waves. He needed to get permission from Madden to make a dash down the river. Since the code books had been destroyed, however, all messages had to be sent in plain English, which the Communists monitored. He sat at his desk for a long time writing a message that he hoped Madden would understand but the Chinese would not:

WOULD BE GRATEFUL YOUR ADVICE ON MY ACTIONS IF MENACED BY THE TYPHOON.

The answer came back:

TYPHOON UNLIKELY REACH YOU IN SERIOUS STRENGTH AND YOU ARE IN GOOD HOLDING GROUND. THE GOLDEN RULE OF MAKING AN OFFING AND TAKING PLENTY OF SEA-ROOM APPLIES PARTICULARLY.

"What do you think that means?" the captain asked Simon. "Seems to me the first sentence says stay where we are but the second says go."

Simon yawned, and Kerans scratched his chin. Simon flopped on the charts and rolled over on his back, his forepaws hanging limp, his bright green eyes looking squarely into the captain's. Kerans rubbed Simon's stomach.

Kerans ordered the ship to be made as secure as possible, and the crew sat around waiting for Gloria.

Sunday night came and went. The weather remained hot and humid. On Monday morning a hot wind began whipping up waves in the brown river surface, and *Amethyst* strained at her anchor cables. All hands except the captain and lieutenants Hett and Strain went below decks. Kerans shut Simon in his cabin. Winds tossed the ship; the anchor chains creaked and groaned. The rain came in sheets, waterfalls and torrents. Rain rattled on the decks like carloads of gravel being dumped. By 9:00 a.m. the wind whipped the ship at between six and seven gale force on the Beaufort scale, or about 25 miles an hour.

Simon didn't move under Captain Kerans' bunk.

The three officers in their oilskins stayed on the bridge, ready to act if the cables should snap. Rains lashed them until they were soaked and water squished out of their shoes when they shifted their feet.

At noon the storm had risen to gale force nine, or 55 miles an hour. The anchor chains creaked. High waves crashed against the ship's sides, rolling over the desks.

By three o'clock the gale force rose to twelve, 75 miles an hour.

Still the cables held.

Then the winds began to blow less fiercely, and the rain slackened. By five o'clock the wind measured gale force nine and the slashing rains began to decrease. At 11:00 p.m. the wind measured seven and it was plain the worst was over.

The men on the bridge went to change into dry clothing. Simon came out from under the bunk and followed his nose to the galley, where Griffiths was starting the first meal he had cooked that day.

When the Moon Sets

*A*methyst survived the typhoon, but her position was becoming more desperate every day. Food was scarce. Yeast for baking bread had gone bad and little flour remained. The crew had been on half rations for two weeks, and very shortly they would have to go on quarter rations. Other supplies were running low, too; there was little disinfectant left and paper for the latrines was running out.

Even more serious was the fuel supply. On the 30th of July there were only fifty-five tons of fuel in the tanks. If Kerans tried to make the 120-mile dash down the river, it would take sixteen tons to turn the ship around in the river; that would leave only thirty-nine tons. Just sitting at anchor used two tons of fuel daily. In a day or two there would not be enough fuel to make the trip. The men and ship would be at the mercy of the Communists.

The captain sat in his cabin looking solemnly at Simon. The lives of seventy-three men and one cat depended on him. "If we don't go tonight," he said to Simon, "I think it will be too late."

He needed a dark, cloudy night to create poor visibility from the shore. The moon was scheduled to set that night at 11:15.

At 3:00 p.m. he called George Strain to his office and shut the door. "Can the ship's engines operate at top speed for eight or nine hours without breaking down?"

Strain looked startled.

"I believe so, sir. The men in the engine room have overhauled all the turbines and replaced the damaged parts."

"Then we are going to make a run for it to-night."

Strain looked stunned.

"The moon sets at 2315 tonight," Kerans continued.

"We need all the darkness we can get. I propose to sail at 2200 hours."

After the typhoon, the British Far East Command developed a new code to send messages. The two men translated a message into code, which they radioed to headquarters. A part of it read:

TOP SECRET. I AM GOING TO TRY AND BREAK OUT 2200 TONIGHT 30th.

At seven o'clock Kerans called all eight Chinese crew members and asked them to follow him to a room below decks where he told them it was necessary for them to be locked up until the next day. "I hated to do that," he told Hett. "But I don't trust them."

At 7:30 p.m. Kerans invited seventeen officers and seamen to his cabin to be told the plans. While Kerans talked, Simon sat at his feet and watched his face. He seemed to sense that something unusual was occurring.

Kerans assigned one group to camouflage the ship, painting her white superstructure black, rigging black canvas from the bridge to the funnel and around the guns to make the ship look like a Landing Ship Tank rather than a frigate. He ordered others to protect the bridge from possible shrapnel splinter damage by wrapping hammocks and mattresses around the bridge railing and even piling up bags of flour like sandbags.

He assigned another group to flood some of the empty fuel tanks to lower the ship in the water. "If the worst happens and the ship is damaged so it cannot be used," Kerans said, "I will attempt to beach her, get the men ashore and then blow up the ship. In that case it will be your duty to get to Shanghai or to the open sea by any means you can."

When he dismissed the grave-faced men, the ship rocked with activity: every man on board had his assignment to carry out before time to sail. Simon stalked about, watching with wonder in his eyes. Everybody's spirits were high.

At about 8:30 p.m. a lookout saw a sampan approaching with vegetables, eggs and beer stores Officer McCarthy had ordered several days before.

Kerans grabbed the intercom. "All hands, stop what you are doing and get about your normal chores at this hour," he shouted. "If the men on the sampan see any unusual activity, they will report it and our whole plan will fail. If you ordinarily would be sleeping at this hour, get the cots out on deck and go to bed.

"Stores, meet the men on the gangplank, unload the supplies and do not allow the sampan men to come on board."

"I'll need But Sai to translate for me."

"No. He must not know we're leaving. He might pass the word to the sampan men."

It seemed like an hour before the sampan arrived.

McCarthy lowered the gangplank and for the seventeen minutes it took to unload the supplies, he kept up a running dialogue with the men although he spoke no Chinese and they spoke no English.

When the supplies were at last unloaded and the men sailed away, the tension eased and crew members scurried around to complete their jobs before time to sail.

Kerans wiped the sweat off his face.

At 9 p.m. he said to Simon, "Come on, I'm going up on the bridge to wait for my eyes to become accustomed to the dark. I wish I could see in the dark as well as you can."

Man and cat climbed the ladder to the bridge. Kerans spoke into the voice pipe. "Men of the *Amethyst*, tonight we begin a flight for our lives. I expect every man to give his utmost to this enterprise. If we are fired on, I will give the smoke order, and I want plenty of it, enough to hide the ship completely. We will keep complete silence. All messages will be flash orders."

That meant any signals sent would be preceded by the word Flash, which meant that the message would get top priority from any ship or radio receiver in the world.

Kerans wiped his face with his handkerchief. The night was hot and muggy.

Simon settled down at Kerans' feet.

Lieutenant Hett, who was navigations officer, saw McNamara, the canteen manager, standing on the deck. He sent a seaman to him with the message. "Lt. Hett wants to see you in the chart house."

When McNamara reported, Hett asked, "Do you know anything about charts?"

"Not a thing."

"Well, you're going to have a chance to learn. Every other man on the ship has his assignment and we can't spare anybody. I want you to stay in the chart house and follow the charts as we go downriver. If the bridge is hit and Captain Kerans disabled, we will still make a run for it. I will call out the landmarks to you on the voice pipe as we pass them. Understand?"

McNamara gulped and nodded.

Down the River

The waning moon went behind a cloud a little after 10:00 p.m. Captain Kerans, standing on the bridge in the darkness, heard a motor throbbing somewhere. In a moment he could make out a ship rounding the curve in the river above them. "Just what we need. A ship to follow," he said in a low tone.

At 10:10 he picked up the voice pipe. "Port engine, half ahead. Slip cable!"

He watched intently. "Starboard engine half astern!"

With one engine churning ahead and one astern and the wheel turning full, the ship reversed in the river in less than a minute.

The ship Kerans had seen, the Kiang Ling *Liberation*, steamed past them and *Amethyst* followed her until a Communist battery on shore shot up a flare. The *Liberation* replied with a siren.

Another flare, meant for *Amethyst*, cut through the darkness.

Amethyst did not reply.

Shells traced arcs into the night above them and fell into the river around them. "Full ahead, both!" ordered Kerans.

The ship tipped to starboard. "We've been hit," Kerans said. He looked around for a place to beach the ship. "Make smoke!" From the vents along the sides of the ship, black clouds of smoke poured out, hiding the vessel.

At 10:33 he sent a flash message for Admiral Brind.

AM UNDER HEAVY FIRE. BEEN HIT.

But then for no apparent reason the ship righted itself and steamed ahead, almost invisible in the dark and smoke. Kerans thought probably a shell exploded in the water so close to the ship that the waves it made tipped the ship.

Kerans took off his shirt and twisting it into a fat rope, he put it around Simon and fastened it to a stanchion. *Amethyst* pushed past *Liberation*, which had turned to port, switching on all her lights and blowing her sirens. A shell whizzed so close to Kerans' neck that he turned around unthinkingly. As he turned, he saw *Liberation* was aground and on fire.

Amethyst sped on through the dark, down the murky, twisting river. Hett listened for the depth sounding reports from the men in the chart room and relayed them to Kerans, who changed the course as the depths grew too shallow. Soon they passed Rose Island, where they had gone aground three months before.

Eleven o'clock came, midnight passed, and all was well except the ship was taking water through one of the shell holes the men had not been able to patch. But the pumps kept up with the flooding.

As the ship neared Kiangyin, the port from which they had sailed 101 days before, a flare lit up the ship and firing from the shore began immediately.

"Make smoke!" Kerans ordered. The thick black smoke poured from her vents, but the firing continued.

At Kiangyin Kerans knew a boom stretched across the river. The boom was composed of a row of sunken ships with only a narrow passageway for a ship to get through.

Kerans peered into the darkness for some sign of the boom as the ship sped full ahead.

A flare lighted up the river and artillery roared.

"Smoke!" ordered Kerans.

The ship rushed on. He reasoned the boom was 500 yards ahead. The ship rushed on full speed, 400 yards, 300 yards, 200 yards. Kerans peered into the blackness.

According to the charts, the passageway through the boom was marked by two lights, pointing the opening through which a ship could safely pass.

There it was. A light. But one light only.

On they went.

Should he go to the left or the right of the light? If he chose the wrong way and crashed into the boom, *Amethyst*'s bottom would be sheered off and she would sink.

The wrong way meant death to the men, death to the ship.

Fifty yards from the boom he took a deep breath. "Pass the light to starboard," he ordered Leslie Frank, the helmsman.

Had he guessed right? He sent up a prayer as he waited for the crash.

The ship slipped through the boom without a scrape.

She steamed on down the river at full speed.

But the danger was not over; the captain knew guns waited for them on both sides of the river farther down.

Soon he radioed Brind he had passed the halfway mark. Brind replied:

IF YOU CANNOT GET PAST WOOSUNG BEFORE DAWN SUGGEST YOU EITHER LAY UP DURING DAYLIGHT OR TAKE THE TSUNG MING CROSSING AND NORTH CHANNEL, WHICH SHOULD BE NAVIGATED AT SLOW SPEED.

At three o'clock Kerans sent out a flash message. ONE HUNDRED UP.

With 100 miles of river behind her, *Amethyst* had only sixty miles to go, but those miles were the closest guarded stretches of river with batteries on both sides.

At 4 a.m. the ship shivered. "We hit something," Kerans said. Simon, who had been snoozing at Kerans' feet, jumped up with a loud "Meow!" In the darkness Kerans saw that *Amethyst* had hit a junk broadside and sliced it in two. He could hear the shouts of people in the water. Ordinarily he would have stopped to give aid, but tonight he could not risk it. "It's all right, Simon," he said. On they sailed.

They still had to pass the heavily guarded shores at Woosung, with a fort on both sides of the river. At 5:03 a.m. they sailed into the danger area. A searchlight swept over the surface of the water.

It passed over the ship.

"Make smoke!"

The light flashed across the ship.

Kerans held his breath. The light passed on. The watchers on the shore had not seen the ship, shrouded in smoke.

They slipped past Woosung at 5:35.

Dawn began lighting the sky.

Kerans spoke over the intercom. "We are almost there. I want every man to give his best," he said. To Simon again asleep at his feet he said, "I think we are going to make it."

At last a lookout shouted, "Destroyer in sight! I think it's one of ours!"

Minutes later he called again. "*Consort* in sight!"

On the *Amethyst* the men began to cheer. Across the water answering cheers came from the crew on *Consort*.

Kerans bent down, untied the shirt and picked Simon up. Hoisting Simon aloft over his head, he shouted, "We made it, Simon! We made it!"

He sent this message to the commander:

HAVE REJOINED THE FLEET. AM SOUTH OF WOOSUNG. NO DAMAGE OR CASUALTIES. GOD SAVE THE KING!

Admiral Brind in return radioed:

WELCOME BACK TO THE FLEET. WE ARE ALL EXTREMELY PROUD OF YOUR MOST GALLANT AND SKILLFUL ESCAPE AND THAT ENDURANCE AND FORTITUDE DISPLAYED BY EVERYONE HAS BEEN REWARDED WITH SUCH SUCCESS. YOUR BEARING IN ADVERSITY AND YOUR DARING PASSAGE TONIGHT WILL BE EPIC IN THE HISTORY OF THE NAVY.

King George VI from Buckingham Palace sent an enthusiastic signal ending, "Splice the mainbrace."

"We'll splice the mainbrace when we heave to in midmorning," Kerans told the crew. "Meanwhile we have a few more hours to go."

As they steamed along, trailed by *Consort*, he called for a reading of the fuel tank. The ship had nine tons left.

They hove to just off the North Saddles. After the drinks Kerans sent the men to bed for a deserved rest.

After 101 days of misery and despair, they loafed all day Sunday, July 31.

A Modest Hero

*N*ext morning the crew assembled on deck for a special presentation. Captain Kerans, the officers and the regular seamen stood at attention.

Mark Allen held Simon in his arms. Facing them, George Griffiths read:

"Able Seaman Simon, for distinguished and meritorious service to HMS *Amethyst* you are hereby awarded the *Amethyst* Campaign Ribbon.

"Be it known that on April 26, 1949, though recovering from wounds, when HMS *Amethyst* was standing by off Rose Bay, you did single-handedly and unarmed stalk down and destroy Mao Tse-Tung, a rat guilty of raiding food supplies which were critically short.

"Be it further known that from April 22 to August 4 you did rid HMS *Amethyst* of pestilence and vermin with unrelenting faithfulness."

He then pinned the ribbon on Simon's collar, saluted and led the crew in "Hip, hip, hooray!"

"I am going to nominate Simon for a Dickin Medal," Kerans said to Griffiths after the ceremony. "All the while we were prisoners on the Yangtze, he worked hard killing rats and saving our food supplies. If that isn't devotion to duty, then nothing is."

"A splendid idea, sir."

That same afternoon he drafted a letter to the PDSA. He wrote:

I wish to nominate Simon, the ship's cat in the H.M.S. *Amethyst* for the Dickin Medal.

When the Communists shelled the ship, Simon was wounded in the back and side and his face was burned. For many days he could not be located. Rats, which began to breed rapidly in the damaged portions of the ship, presented a real menace to the health of the ship's company, but Simon nobly rose to the occasion and after two months the rats were much diminished.

Throughout the incident Simon's behavior was of the highest order. One would not have expected a small cat to have survived the blast from an explosion capable of making a hole over a foot in diameter in a steel plate. Yet after a few days Simon was as good as ever. His presence in the ship was a decided factor in maintaining the high level of morale in the ship's company.

He sent off the letter by post, and then the ship sailed down the China coast to Hong Kong, arriving just before noon on Wednesday, August 3. Hundreds of British citizens waiting on the docks cheered the ship as they steamed into the harbor.

Simon, D. M.

$\mathcal{T}$he brave and miraculous escape of the
Amethyst brought instant fame to the officers and crew of
the ship. Although little had been reported in the
Western newspapers and on radio while the ship was in
the Yangtze, once she escaped, the story of her harrow-
ing days in the Yangtze and the flight downriver was
reported in great detail. Kerans and the crew became
instant heroes.

Two weeks after they arrived in Hong Kong the
PDSA reply was delivered to the ship in dock:

The Awards Committee of the PDSA is unani-
mous in conferring the Dickin Medal on Simon, the
Amethyst's ships' cat. He becomes the first cat to hold the
Dickin Medal. This is also the first time that the award
has gone to the Royal Navy.

It is hoped to arrange a presentation ceremony for Simon when *Amethyst* returns home.

In the meantime the PDSA sent a tricolor ribbon collar for Simon to wear.

The PDSA also released the news of Simon's award to the world press.

News reporters and photographers hurried to the ship. The reporters interviewed Captain Kerans and the men, but it was Simon the photographers liked best. The little black and white cat's photograph appeared in hundreds of newspapers and news magazines and flashed on the movie news screens. Who can resist a winsome cat? The ship was swamped with visitors and letters from all over the world. Poems praising Simon's bravery came in every mail, and all manner of packages of food and toys arrived. For weeks he received more than 200 pieces of mail a day.

Captain Kerans appointed Lt. Hett "Cat's Officer" to answer Simon's mail.

All the while Simon remained unimpressed with the attention. He posed reluctantly for pictures and continued to kill rats.

One day a newspaper photographer saw him marching down the gangplank with a look of knowing where he was going on his face. He snapped his picture. Then the photographer went aboard to take a picture of Captain Kerans. "Got a good shot of your cat," he said, "walking down the gangplank."

"Walking down the gangplank? Simon? Black and white cat?"

"That's the one."

Captain Kerans rushed out of his cabin and down the deck to the gangplank. He stood at the top and called. "Simon! Simon!"

But Simon was gone.

He dashed to the bridge and picked up the microphone. "All hands on deck! All hands on deck!"

Sailors came running from every direction.

"Some damn fool left the gangplank down and Simon went ashore," he said. "I want every one of you to go at once and fan out through the city and alleys and find him.

"Bring him back! Understand? Find that cat and bring him back. I want you all back within an hour and with Simon!"

The men hurried down the gangplank and scattered through streets and alleys of Hong Kong. When they straggled back at the end of an hour, nobody had seen Simon.

The captain went into his cabin and closed the door.

Three hours later Griffiths, who had stationed himself at the head of the gangplank, saw Simon stroll out of an alley and head up the gangplank. He grabbed him and took him to the captain.

Captain Kerans took Simon into his arms and kissed him on the nose.

He picked up the voice pipe and called, "Simon is back! Splice the mainbrace!"

One More Voyage

Photographers and visitors continued to troop onto the ship, and Simon was wakened from many an afternoon's nap to pose for the photographers. Reporters interviewed crew members about him, but he yawned and squirmed to get away from them. He did what he liked doing best. He patrolled the ship, visited the sick bay, ate in the galley and kept on killing rats.

At last the ship's repairs were finished, and *Amethyst* sailed for England and home. It was a triumphal journey, and at every port where the ship stopped in the Indian Ocean, the Suez Canal, and the Mediterranean, cheering crowds gathered and more reporters came aboard with their photographers and flash guns. The ship finally reached Plymouth November 1, 1949.

British law requires that all animals entering the country must be quarantined for six months. Captain Kerans took Simon to the quarantine kennels at Hackbridge, Surrey.

"I'll come visit you often, Simon," he said as the attendant put Simon into a cage. "And when the time is up, I will come for you."

He rubbed Simon's back and tousled his ears and walked away. The city of London had planned a parade to honor the men of the ship, and King George was giving an audience for the officers.

Mark Allen came in his wheelchair to see Simon before he left for London. "I am going to get new legs," he told Simon. "As soon as I learn to walk, the first place I will come is here to see you. If it hadn't been for you, I think they would have buried me at sea." He hugged Simon and kissed him and reluctantly put him back in his cage. On his way out, he gave the hairbrush to the kennel maid. "Will you groom Simon?" he asked her. "He likes to be brushed every morning after breakfast."

"I will," she replied.

"You promise?"

"I promise."

Mark wheeled to the door. He turned around and looked at Simon, sitting in a corner of his cage. "Goodbye, Simon." He turned and the door shut behind him.

Mail and gifts for Simon arrived with every post. Four cats in Chelsea sent a poem:

> O Simon of the *Amethyst*,
> Stout member of her crew,
> We fill our saucers high with milk
> And drink a health to you;
> What though cannon roar and thunder,
> Your courage ne'er went under.
> For England, home and beauty
> You are steadfast in your duty
> As terror of the rats!
> So here's a greeting and congrats
> From four admiring Chelsea cats.

Miss Louise Edwards, keeper of the hotel cats at Arden Hotel, Birmingham, sent a package. "We are sending you this tin of sardines which we hope you will enjoy," said the card with it. "With good wishes from Smoky, Peter and Kit."

Visitors came by the scores to the quarantine kennels.

Simon received the best of treatment while he was in quarantine. Joyce Rallack, the kennel maid, brought him a toy, a mouse on a stick, and played with him every day. And mindful of her promise, she groomed Simon with Mark's hairbrush.

The Lord Mayor of London was to come to Hackbridge for the medal presentation December 11. Seventy-nine-year old Maria Dickin, founder of the PDSA, also planned to be present.

On Sunday, four days before the presentation was scheduled, the kennel maid noticed that Simon seemed listless. He slept most of the time and didn't want to play. His nose felt warm.

First thing next morning Joyce Ballack spoke to the superintendent of the kennel. As soon as he looked at Simon, he went to his office and telephoned the Royal College of Veterinary Surgeons in London. "We have a sick cat here," he said, "Simon of the *Amethyst*. He isn't eating, and his nose is warm. Will you send somebody?"

Within the hour a doctor arrived. He put Simon on a table and felt his nose. He looked in his ears and his eyes. Then he rubbed exploring hands over his body. When he touched Simon just over his back legs, Simon let out a howl. "Does it hurt there, boy?"

The doctor took a thermometer from his pocket and slipped it into the opening under Simon's tail. Simon winced and growled. "I know it doesn't feel good, boy, but the worst is over."

In a little while he took out the thermometer and looked at it. "His temperature is 104," he said. "He has picked up a virus. Enteritis. I will give him two shots and leave some medicine."

The first shot didn't hurt. Simon growled when he gave him the second one. "He's a sick cat, but he ought to be better in the morning. Give him these pills I'm leaving, one tonight and one in the morning. I will be back in the morning at 10."

Joyce decided to stay with Simon all night. For several hours he lay on his side and seemed to be sleeping. But finally she reached out her hand and stroked him. His heart had stopped beating.

She ran to the telephone to rouse the superintendent.

When the surgeon came in the morning, he said. "I think that Simon never fully recovered from his wounds. His heart was weak. What a brave little fellow he was."

The surgeon telephoned the news to Captain Kerans, who was on the ship at Plymouth. "Dead? Simon dead?" exclaimed the captain. "How can that be? What happened?"

"He picked up a virus," the surgeon said. "I gave him medication, but his heart was weak from his wounds."

"Poor Simon. He went right on working in all that heat, and he must have felt terrible. If only I had known . . ." The captain's voice broke. "I shall miss him," he went on. "All the men on the ship will miss him."

The news flashed out over radio and in newspapers. Stories and editorials appeared in scores of newspapers. His picture appeared in *Time Magazine* under the heading "In Honored Memory." Sympathy cards and letters and flowers arrived by the truckload at Hackbridge.

For a Hero

*R*osalind Evans, reading the newspaper over her second cup of tea while Ruth and Clara washed up the tea dishes, set down her cup. "I have had a brilliant idea," she said.

It had been a long time since she had one.

"What's that?" asked Ruth.

"Well, you remember reading about Simon, the cat on the *Amethyst*, don't you?"

"Of course," answered Clara. "He won the Dickin Medal."

"What about him?" asked Ruth.

"He's dead."

"He died?" Ruth seemed surprised; Clara made little sympathetic noises. "But he was only a young cat. Not like Faith."

"He hasn't even had his medal presented yet," Ruth said. "What happened?"

"He picked up a virus. The vet said he never completely recovered from his wounds."

"Poor little fellow. What's your idea?"

"My idea is for us to go to Ilford when they bury him and attend his funeral. In memory of Faith."

"When is the funeral?"

"The paper doesn't say. I will ring up the PDSA officer at Ilford and find out."

Rosalind rang and when the officer at the clinic answered the telephone, he told her that Simon would be buried the next afternoon.

"What kind of services are you having?" Rosalind asked.

"Services? He has a casket with a Union Jack to cover it."

"I see," Rosalind said. "Well, that is nice, but aren't there going to be prayers and readings?"

Evidently not. "This is Rosalind Evans," she said. "I am part of the altar guild at St. Augustine's in

London. St. Augustine's is the church where Faith, who also received a medal from the PDSA, lived. You may have read about Faith. Mrs. Dickin herself presented her with a medal, and the Archbishop came to the presentation. It was in all the papers. Four years ago."

The person remembered Faith.

"Father Henry Ross, the rector of St. Augustine's, did a very fine service for Faith, and I am sure he would do one for Simon, too. Would you like that?"

She took a quick drink of tea while she listened.

"That's right," she said, nodding. "Tomorrow at three? I'll tell Father Ross, and if I don't call you back, we will be there."

The PDSA Pet Cemetery at Ilford is a grassy stretch of land on the edge of the village. An arched wrought iron gate stands at the entrance and over the gate are the words "They Also Serve."

Everywhere to left and right are little graves of pets, many with markers or tombstones.

An open grave stood not far from the gate. The small casket covered by a Union Jack stood at one side. Baskets and sprays of flowers edged the plot.

Henry, Thomas, Rosalind, Ruth, and Clara joined several staff members from the PDSA and two ladies from the village. Just as they were about to gather around the grave, a handsome young man in a navy uniform with H.M.S. *AMETHYST* on his cap walked slowly into the cemetery and joined them. He used crutches, but he stood tall and the shoes on his feet shone in the sun. Thomas shook hands with the lad.

"You were on the *Amethyst*?" he asked.

"Yes, I was. I know Simon well. He visited me every day when I was in the hospital on board ship. I loved him."

"What is your name?"

"Mark Allen."

"Would you like to read one of the Psalms today, Mark?"

"I would be proud to."

Henry nodded at Thomas, who handed Mark his Bible. Henry stepped to the head of the grave.

"The Lord be with you," he said.

"And with thy spirit," the little group responded.

"Let us pray."

Henry read the collect for the Sunday closest to November 28, which was the very day Simon died: "O

God, who declarest thy almighty power in showing
mercy and pity: Mercifully grant us such a measure of
thy grace that we, running to obtain thy promises, may
be made partakers of thy heavenly treasure; through
Jesus Christ our Lord, who liveth and reigneth with thee
and the holy Spirit, one God, for ever and ever. Amen."

He looked at Mark and nodded.

"The Lord is my shepherd," Mark began reading
in a young voice; "I shall not want.

"He makes me to lie down in green pastures; he
leads me beside the still waters."

A shaft of sunlight filtered through the trees and
lighted the red, white, and blue flag on the small coffin.

Mark finished the psalm and closed the book.

Henry read the consecration for Simon's grave
as he had for Faith's: "O God, whose blessed Son was
laid in a sepulcher in the garden: Bless, we pray, this
grave, and grant that he whose body is to be buried here
may dwell with Christ in paradise, and may come to
your heavenly kingdom; through your son Jesus Christ
our Lord. Amen."

Ruth and Clara lowered the box into the grave,
and Thomas and Rosalind shoveled the earth in on top

of it. At the head of the grave a PDSA officer placed a temporary wooden marker which read "In honoured memory of Simon, D. M. H.M.S. *Amethyst*. Died November 28th, 1949."

Henry turned again to his book. "Rest eternal grant to him, O Lord," he read, "and may light perpetual shine upon him. May his soul and the souls of all the departed, through the mercy of God, rest in Peace. Amen.

"Alleluia. Christ is risen."

The little group responded, "The Lord is risen indeed. Alleluia."

Henry closed his book and held up his hand. "Let us go forth in the name of the Lord."

"Thanks be to God."

The PDSA officers set about banking the flowers on the grave, and Henry, Thomas, Mark and the women walked out of the gate and into the town. They walked slowly because of Mark's halting gait.

"Where do you live?" Henry asked him.

"London. I came down on the train."

"So did we. Let's go back together and have a little something at the church," said Henry. "We would like for Mark to tell us about Simon and what happened on the *Amethyst*. Will you come, Mark?"

"I'll put on the big tea pot," said Rosalind. "And Ruth and Clara will make some chicken sandwiches. How about it, Mark?"

"I would love to come."

And that's exactly what they did.

Afterword

*L*ater two women of Ilford commissioned a sculptor to design the stone monument which now marks Simon's grave in the pet cemetery at Ilford. The inscription on the monument says

In Memory of Simon
Served in
H M S *Amethyst*
May 1948 – September 1949
Awarded Dickin Medal
August 1949
Died 28th November 1949
THROUGHOUT THE "YANGTZE INCIDENT" HIS
BEHAVIOUR WAS OF THE HIGHEST ORDER

His medal was awarded posthumously to
Captain and Mrs. Kerans by the Admiral of the Fleet.
Captain Kerans presented the medal to the Naval
Museum in Portsmouth so that visitors could see it.

Many years later the medal was sold to a private
collector in Canada.

In 1993 it was put up for auction at Christie's in
London. It was expected to bring between 3,000 and
5,000 pounds. Lieutenant Commander Stewart Hett
attended the auction and put in a bid for it, but the price
kept going up and up until he had to drop out. The
Eaton Film Company of London, which had made a TV
film called "Animal Heroes" and in which Simon
appears, bought it for 23,000 pounds for display pur-
poses. It is kept in the company's safety vault.

Resources

Books

The Book of Common Prayer. New York: Henry Holt and Company, 1932.

Bourne, Dorothea St. Hill. *They Also Serve*. London: Winchester Publications, Limited, 1950.

Deighton, Len. *The Battle of Britain*. London: Winchester Publications, Limited, 1950.

Earl, Lawrence. *Yangtse Incident*. New York: Alfred A. Knopf, 1951.

Gooden, Mona, ed. *The Poet's Cat*. Freeport, NY: Books for Libraries Press, 1946.

The Hymnal 1982. New York: The Church Hymnal Corporation, 1985.

Murfett, Malcolm H. *Hostage in the Yangtze*. Annapolis: Naval Institute Press, 1991.

Roman Ritual Book of Blessings. New York: Catholic Book Publishing Co., 1989.

Wood, Gerald L. *Guinness Book of Pet Records*. London: Guinness Superlatives, 1984.

Magazines

"Flight of the Amethyst." *Newsweek,* August 8, 1949.

Kent, George. "Epic of the Amethyst." *The Reader's Digest,* May, 1950.

"King's Navee." *Newsweek*, November 14, 1949.

"Ordeal on the River." *Time*, May 31, 1952.

"Reds Shell British out of the Yangtze." *Life*, May 9, 1949.

"Shore Battery." *Time*, May 2, 1949.

"Splice the Mainbrace." *Time*, August 8, 1949.

Interviews

Lt. Cmdr. Stewart Hett, president of the *Amethyst* Association and Cat's Officer. London, March 18, 1994.

Gill Hubbard, PDSA Headquarters, Telford, March 17, 1994.

Newspapers

O'Shea, Suzanne. "Puss in Boot's Medal of Honour." *Daily Mail,* February 11, 1993.

"Devasted Churches — A Crime for which Goering Must Answer." *The Illustrated London News,* September 10, 1940.

"While H.M.S. '*Amethyst* 'Lay Detained on the Yangtse." *The Illustrated London News,* November 26, 1949.

Pamphlets

"The Dickin Medal, the Animals' V. C." PDSA, Telford, no date.
"Maria Dickin." PDSA, Telford, no date.
Ross, Henry. "Faith." London, 1950.

Scrapbooks

Lt. Cmdr. John S. Kerans' Scrapbook. 2 volumes. Imperial War Museum, London.
Lt. Cmdr. Stewart Hett's scrapbooks in Hett's library, Middlesex.